THE CHILDREN OF DICKENS

DAVID COPPERFIELD AND PEGGOTTY BY THE PARLOUR FIRE

THE CHILDREN OF DICKENS

SAMUEL McCHORD CROTHERS

ILLUSTRATED BY

JESSIE WILLCOX SMITH

NEW YORK
CHARLES SCRIBNER'S SONS

CONTENTS

		PAGE
I.	LONDON ONCE UPON A TIME	1
II.	DICKENS HIMSELF	9
III.	PIP *Pierre & Claude*	17
	PIP AT MR. PUMBLECHOOK'S	26
IV.	DAVID COPPERFIELD	27
	THE LITTLE BOY AND THE HUNGRY WAITER	36
V.	WILKINS MICAWBER JUNIOR AND HIS PARENTS	43
VI.	ON THE ROAD TO DOVER	59
VII.	JOE THE FAT BOY	69
VIII.	OLIVER TWIST	77
IX.	THE JELLYBY CHILDREN	89
X.	SISSY JUPE	101
XI.	THE CHILD OF THE MARSHALSEA	109
XII.	THE CRATCHITS	115
XIII.	THE DOLL'S DRESSMAKER	123
XIV.	LITTLE NELL	131
	THE JOLLY SANDBOYS	135
	MRS. JARLEY AND HER WAX-WORKS	139
XV.	THE KENWIGSES	149
XVI.	THE CHILD'S STORY	155
XVII.	THE BOY AT TODGERS'S	163

CONTENTS

		PAGE
XVIII.	THE DOMBEY CHILDREN	171
	HOW FLORENCE DOMBEY WAS LOST IN LONDON	176
	PAUL DOMBEY AT BRIGHTON	187
XIX.	JEMMY JACKMAN LIRRIPER'S STORY	193
XX.	ON THE WAY TO GRETNA GREEN	203
XXI.	OUR SCHOOL	209
XXII.	ALICIA IN WONDERLAND	223
XXIII.	THE INFANT PHENOMENON	241
XXIV.	A CHRISTMAS TREE	249

LIST OF ILLUSTRATIONS

David Copperfield and Peggotty by the Parlour Fire . . . *Frontispiece*

FACING PAGE

Pip and Joe Gargery 20

Little Em'ly 36

Oliver's First Meeting with the Artful Dodger 84

Tiny Tim and Bob Cratchit on Christmas Day 118

Jenny Wren, the Little Doll's Dressmaker 126

Little Nell and Her Grandfather at Mrs. Jarley's 133

Mrs. Kenwigs and the Four Little Kenwigses 152

Paul Dombey and Florence on the Beach at Brighton 173

The Runaway Couple 205

The cover lining and title-page decoration designed by Euphame Mallison.

LONDON ONCE UPON A TIME

I

LONDON ONCE UPON A TIME

ONCE there was a city called Bagdad. I know just how it looked, and so do you. It was very mysterious. It was on a mysterious river called the Tigris. There were a great many little canals running in every direction through the city. The drinking water was brought to the houses in goatskins carried on the backs of men. These water-carriers often turned out to be very interesting persons. On the banks of the river were palm-trees, and under every palm-tree was a dervish or two. The streets of the city were narrow and winding, and dark people in flowing robes flitted about on secret errands that aroused suspicion. One could never tell what they were up to. There was Haroun Al Raschid prowling around with his grand vizier and his executioner. He was full of curiosity, and had a keen sense of justice. In Bagdad everything turned out in a most remarkable way. If you were looking for one mystery, you would find half a dozen.

I have recently read an article by a gentleman who has lived a number of years in Bagdad, and it appears that he has not seen any of the wonderful things that I am interested in. He says that the climate is very uncomfortable and that the thermometer often stands at 112 degrees at breakfast-time. That is very hot indeed. He says that many of the people now go about in Ford cars instead of riding on camels.

[3]

When they want excitement they go to the movies. In short, according to his account, Bagdad must be getting to be very much like other places.

All this is disappointing, but as I am never likely to go to the modern Bagdad, anyway, it doesn't matter so much to me. My Bagdad is in the *Arabian Nights*, and I can still go to it whenever I feel so inclined. When I open the book I find everything just as it was "once upon a time."

It is the same with London. When I first crossed the Atlantic and visited the great city, I was a bit troubled because many parts of it looked so much like other places. I wanted it to be like the London I had read about. Of course this wasn't fair to the people who live there, who can't be expected to keep it just for travellers to look at.

When I think of London as it was once upon a time, that is the time when Charles Dickens lived in it. This London was as wonderful as Bagdad, though in different ways. If you want to know what it was like, you must go to the Dickens books. Dickens was the only one who ever saw London in that way. When you ask whether it was the real London, you have to take his word for it. It was real to him and he had the power to make it real to us. That is what we call genius.

The London the Dickens people lived in was a big city, so big that one easily got lost in it. The railroads were just coming in, but they didn't get into the stories. There were no telephones or electric lights or automobiles or radios. People came in from the green country on gay stage-coaches with prodigious tooting of horns and cracking of whips. They stopped at inns, where a great deal of eating and drinking was going on. But when they left the inns to explore the town, they plunged into a maze of the queerest streets imaginable. The streets ran in every direction except in the direction one wanted to go. Many of them were mere alleys, but they were always crowded. One soon got down to the river, where there were old warehouses that leaned over the water but never actually fell in. There were old and shabby houses, and the people were made to match them. That is what made them so interesting and exciting. Yet, though there were so many people on the streets that you didn't know, it was curious to be all the time running across people you did know, or who knew you. If you were trying to hide, you were sure to be found out. On the other hand, you could get lost with no difficulty at all.

One of the most interesting parts of the city to prowl around in was down by the water-front. The River Thames flowed through London just as mysteriously as the River Tigris flowed by Bagdad; and it was the scene of many adventures. To be sure, there were no palm-trees and no dervishes. But there were great ships coming from countries as far away as Arabia and the Spice Islands. On the banks of the river were great warehouses, with musty, mouldy cellars and strange garrets, and with all kinds of foreign smells. Back from the river were streets where people lived who could afford to live nowhere else. Some of them were dwarfed, with gnarled faces, as if they had not had sunlight enough when they were growing up. Some of these people were as bad as they looked, but many of them were much better. When you had time to become acquainted with them, you couldn't help but like them. Each person had some little trick of manner which made it easy to recognize him. They had a way of doing the same thing over again, just as people have in real life. This made them amusing even when we could not approve of them.

Most of the people we meet live in lodgings — which is a very interesting way to live in England. You hire a room and the landlady will go out and buy the food for you and serve it in your room. This gives opportunity for a good deal of conversation. It's all very snug and cosey if you have money to pay for what you order. If you haven't, this leads to more conversation. Many of the Dickens people didn't have a very regular income and were not sure where the next meal was coming from. Having a good dinner was quite an event to them, and they made the most of it. It is wonderful the enjoyment they got out of eating and drinking. And how they liked to talk on such happy occasions! They were living in a hand-to-mouth way, but they didn't seem to mind it as much as people in the world outside of the Dickens books do. They took it all as an adventure.

Down in the city were the offices of the bankers and rich merchants, where clerks sat on high stools and did their accounts under the eyes of elderly gentlemen whom they didn't like. In the suburbs there were trim little houses where people lived who were beginning to be more prosperous.

LONDON ONCE UPON A TIME

One doesn't see much of the great places. Though there were palaces in London, the people whom Dickens was interested in didn't live in them, though they admired them very much and were proud of them in a way. For they were every-day Englishmen who lived in the days of good Queen Victoria.

The great thing about London as Dickens saw it, and as we see it through his eyes, was that it was queer. The houses were queer, and the streets were queer, and the people were queer. Each one went about his business without caring a rap for what other people thought about him. If they acted in a particular way, it was because they were made that way. And yet they were friendly — most of them. And those that weren't were such villains and hypocrites that we dislike them heartily. We always know just what to think about them, and so we don't waste any sympathy on them. When the characters appear, we know at once which ones are to be looked upon with suspicion and which are to be trusted. You get to know the people in Dickens's London because he is so anxious to make you see them as plainly as he does. If you don't see them at first, he keeps on telling about them till you can't help yourself.

Now if I were to tell you that I saw a child with a face like a rosy apple, you would probably forget all about it in a minute or so. But Dickens goes at the business of description more thoroughly. He says:

"Miss Tox escorted a plump rosy-cheeked, apple-faced young woman, with an infant in her arms, and a younger

[7]

woman not so plump but apple-faced also, who led a plump and apple-faced child in each hand, another plump and apple-faced boy who walked by himself, and finally a plump and apple-faced man who carried another plump and apple-faced boy, whom he stood down on the floor and admonished in a husky whisper to ketch hold of his brother Johnny."

When I see the happy apple-faced family together, it makes an impression on me. It's the same with the descriptions of the scenery or the weather. I might say that the London fog is very disagreeable, and you would answer that you had always heard so. But Dickens takes you out into the fog and you see it and feel it and taste it:

"Fog everywhere. Fog up the river where it flows among the green meadows. Fog down the river where it rolls defiled among the tiers of shipping and the waterside pollutions of a great and dirty city. Fog in the Essex marshes, fog on the Kentish heights. Fog creeping into the cabooses of collier brigs, fog lying out on the yards and hovering in the rigging of great ships; fog in the eyes and throats of ancient Green-wich pensioners wheezing by the firesides in their wards; fog in the stem and bowl of the afternoon pipe of the wrath-ful skipper down in the close cabin."

By this time you get the London fog into your own throat and feel what it was like in November, when "the raw afternoon is rawest and the dense fog is densest and the muddiest streets are muddiest." When you feel all this, Dickens is ready to go on with his story.

[8]

DICKENS HIMSELF

II

DICKENS HIMSELF

I ONCE sat with several thousand people on one summer
evening to watch an historical pageant at Warwick in
England. Back of us were the walls of the great Norman
castle, around us were the old trees that had been there for
centuries, and through the trees we could see the little River
Avon. Then the townspeople acted out for us the romantic
scenes that had taken place on that very spot. First we saw
the Druids building their altars; then the Romans came; and
after them the Saxons. After a while we saw Norman knights
riding under the greenwood trees. Warwick the king-maker
rode up to his castle. Then there was a stir on the river, and
we saw Queen Elizabeth in her barge. When she had been
received in state, the officers of the neighboring towns were
presented to her. Among them was Mr. Shakespeare from
Stratford, who brought with him his young son, William.
Then came Cromwell's soldiers and the men who have made
history since Queen Elizabeth's day.

It was all very picturesque, and we felt that we were really
watching the events that had taken place on that spot through
the centuries of English history. But when the Druids and
the Saxons and the Normans and the great personages of
every degree had passed out of our sight, there was only one

person left. It was the little boy from Stratford. He stood there all alone, thinking it all over. Then he walked away.

Now the thing that made the most impression upon us was this boy who had the gift of seeing all we saw and more in his imagination. For, after all, the great thing about the River Avon is that this boy once played upon its banks. And the pleasant Warwickshire country has for its chief charm the fact that William Shakespeare knew it and loved it.

Now and then a person is born who has the gift not only of seeing things more clearly than we do, but of making us see them more vividly than we could without his help. Such a person we call a genius. He gives us the use of his mind. When such a person writes a book, it is as if he had created an interesting country and filled it with all sorts of things for our amusement. He invites us to visit him and make ourselves at home. And the best of it is that we are not invited for a particular day. The invitation is open to us for a lifetime. Whenever we feel inclined, we may visit Shakespeare's country and meet all the Shakespearian people and listen to their talk. And the more often we go on such visits, the more enjoyment we find.

Now it is the same with Dickens. To be sure, his hospitality is not on so grand a scale as Shakespeare's. He does not show us kings, or knights in armor, or vast parks and lordly castles. But he opens to us a world of imagination that is his own. It is filled with common people, but they are uncommonly amusing. We see not only what they are doing, but also what they think they are doing, which is often absurdly different. We see their "tricks and their manners" as they cannot possibly see them. That is where we have the advantage of them. Some of them strut about as if they owned the earth, while some that wear poor clothes and endure hard knocks turn out to be the real heroes. Dickens is not like some writers who pride themselves on not telling what they think of their characters. He has his likes and his dislikes, and he doesn't care who knows it. He hates a bully, whether he is a man or boy, and he loves the people who knock the bully down. That is because he suffered so much from bullies when he was a boy.

When he was twelve years old, his father lost his money and was thrown into a debtors' prison. It was a queer way they had then of treating a person who couldn't pay his debts. They shut him up where he couldn't earn anything. Charles had to visit pawn-shops to try to borrow money for the family. Then he was put to work in a big, gloomy establishment where they made blacking for shoes. His work was to sit all day on a bench pasting labels on the boxes. Then he would have to find ways of keeping alive on a few pennies he got each day.

But though he had a very hard time for a year or two, he spent his time greatly to his own and our advantage. Before he was thirteen, he had accumulated a great deal of experience. He had kept his eyes open and had seen a side of life that most people never see at all.

When I think of Dickens and of his way of finding out obscure people, and making them interesting, I remember the advice I once read in a newspaper as to how to find a collar-button. When a collar-button rolls off the dressing-table, it seems to have an uncanny way of rolling out of sight. The gentleman who is in need of it feels himself greatly aggrieved over the collar-button's easy way of getting lost. Now the newspaper man said that the reason the man doesn't see the collar-button is that he stands too high above it. If he will forget all about his dignity and lie down on the floor, he can't help but see what he is looking for. In order to see it he must get down to the level where the collar-button is. There he will see it shining like a little mountain of gold.

I think that explains why Dickens sees so much more in his characters than other persons would who did not have his advantages. He does not look down on his characters. He meets them on their own level, because he has been there. And so he makes us see them.

He learned very early that, no matter where a person is, he is always the centre of his little world. He always has something that he is afraid of and always has something that he hopes for. And he learned to sympathize not only with the big hopes and fears but with the little hopes and fears. They are the things which wise people often overlook, but they are really very important, for there are so many of them.

Dickens did not write children's stories, that is, stories about children who stayed as children. Of course there are children in his novels just as there are in the London streets — plenty of them. But they are all mixed up with the older people. And then they are all the time growing up just as they do in real life. You get acquainted with a small boy in one chapter; and the next time you meet him he is at boarding-school, and before the end of the book he is out walking with children of his own.

This is the reason why it would not be worth while to try to tell the stories of the children in the novels of Dickens. The moment you got to the most exciting part of the story you would find that they weren't children at all. They are quite grown up. The fact is that Dickens was not very much of a story-teller. We do not read him for the plot, which is often hard to follow. He gives us scenes, one after another, each one really complete in itself.

When we sit down by the fire on a winter evening, some one says: "What shall we read? We haven't time to read a book through — only a chapter." Now the chances are that we choose a chapter from Dickens. And it's very likely that we will choose some scene which we all are most familiar with.

We come into an inn. The coach has just arrived, and there is a cheerful bustle. We hear the blowing of the horns and the cracking of the whips, and if Mr. Weller happens to be driver, or if Mr. Pickwick and his friends happen to be on board, we are sure that we will be left in a state of great good humor.

Or we drop into a shabby little house, and climb the stairs till we come to a room where some of our friends are having a little dinner. They are making speeches to one another, and acting in a most extraordinary manner. It's their way of having a good time, and we are glad that they can enjoy themselves over so little.

We hear people quarrelling and crying and laughing, and we are curious to know what it is all about. The best of it is that Dickens always tells us. If a man is a villain, we see it at once; and if he is a good-hearted person, we give him credit for it. We do not have to read the book through to get the flavor of it. We go at once to the scenes that please us best.

The scenes that are selected for this book are those in which children appear, and we want to see them as Dickens did.

PIP

III

PIP

AS I have said, almost all the Dickens people lived in London or went up to it sometimes. But all were not born there, and many of them, as children, lived in little villages. When they got to be seventeen or eighteen, they went to the great city to seek their fortunes.

There was Pip. I don't care so much for him after he grew up. When he got to London he became very much like other folks. I like him best when he was a small boy in the country.

His name was Philip Pirrip. This was hard to pronounce, and puckered up the lips like "Peter Piper picked a peck of peppers." The best he could make of it was Pip, and so everybody called him that for short.

His father and mother had died, and he was brought up by his older sister, who had married Joe Gargery, the blacksmith. She was twenty years older than Pip and had forgotten how she felt when she was his age. This made trouble for them both.

Pip had a hard time with Mrs. Gargery, and so had Joe, and so they became great chums. Joe was a big man, and his arms were strong, as all blacksmiths' are, but he had never learned to read and write, though he knew some of the letters of the alphabet and was very proud over that.

The house where the Gargerys lived was in the marsh country near a river. One could look out on a dark flat country with little ditches running through it in every direction. It was a place where one could easily get lost, and where robbers could hide. There was a prison ship down near the mouth of the river, and now and then some of the prisoners would escape and get into the marsh. Pip met two of them once and had an exciting adventure. Down by the river there was a battery, and Pip used to go down with Joe Gargery sometimes and sit on the old cannon, while Joe would tell what fine things they would do if Mrs. Joe would let them. But she never did let them do what they wanted to do if she could prevent it.

Pip went to an evening school taught by an old lady who also kept a little store in the same room. He didn't learn very much, for the old lady used to go to sleep most of the time. But as she only charged four cents a week, Mrs. Joe thought it was cheap enough. It was in this school that Pip learned the alphabet, and he was very proud when he found that he could put the letters together to make words. He wanted to know whether Joe had learned to read, and Joe did not want him to find out. One night they were sitting in the chimney corner, and with great effort Pip printed a letter which he handed to Joe. He tells how the letter was received.

WHY JOE DID NOT KNOW HOW TO READ

"mI deEr JO i opE U r krWitE wEll i opE i shAl soN B haBelL 4 2 teeDge U JO aN theN wE shOrl b sO glOdd aN wEn i M preNgtD 2 u JO woT larX an blEvE ME inF xn PiP."

PIP AND JOE GARGERY

There was no indispensable necessity for my communicating with Joe by letter, inasmuch as he sat beside me and we were alone. But, I delivered this written communication (slate and all) with my own hand, and Joe received it, as a miracle of erudition.

"I say, Pip, old chap!" cried Joe, opening his blue eyes wide, "what a scholar you are! Ain't you?"

"I should like to be," said I, glancing at the slate as he held it: with a misgiving that the writing was rather hilly.

"Why, here's a J," said Joe, "and an O equal to anythink! Here's a J and an O, Pip, and a J–O, Joe."

I had never heard Joe read aloud to any greater extent than this monosyllable, and I had observed at church last Sunday, when I accidentally held our Prayer-Book upside down, that it seemed to suit his convenience quite as well as if it had been all right. Wishing to embrace the present occasion of finding out whether in teaching Joe, I should have to begin quite at the beginning, I said, "Ah! But read the rest, Joe."

"The rest, eh, Pip?" said Joe, looking at it with a slowly searching eye. "One, two, three. Why, here's three J's, and three O's, and three J–O, Joes, in it, Pip!"

I leaned over Joe, and, with the aid of my forefinger, read him the whole letter.

"Astonishing!" said Joe, when I had finished. "You ARE a scholar."

"How do you spell Gargery, Joe?" I asked him, with a modest patronage.

"I don't spell it at all," said Joe.

"But supposing you did?"

"It *can't* be supposed," said Joe. "Tho' I'm uncommon fond of reading, too."

"Are you, Joe?"

"On-common. Give me," said Joe, "a good book, or a good newspaper, and sit me down afore a good fire, and I ask no better. Lord!" he continued, after rubbing his knees a little. "When you *do* come to a J and a O, and says you, 'Here, at last, is a J–O, Joe,' how interesting reading is!"

I derived from this last, that Joe's education, like Steam, was yet in its infancy. Pursuing the subject, I inquired:

"Didn't you ever go to school, Joe, when you were as little as me?"

"No, Pip."

"Why didn't you ever go to school, Joe, when you were as little as me?"

"Well, Pip," said Joe, taking up the poker, and settling himself to his usual occupation when he was thoughtful, of slowly raking the fire between the lower bars: "I'll tell you. My father, Pip, he were given to drink, and when he were overtook with drink, he hammered away at my mother most onmerciful. It were a'most the only hammering he did, indeed, 'xcepting at myself. And he hammered at me with a wigor only to be equalled by the wigor with which he didn't hammer at his anwil. You're a-listening and understanding, Pip?"

"Yes, Joe."

" 'Consequence, my mother and me we ran away from my father several times; and then my mother she'd go out to work, and she'd say, 'Joe,' she'd say, 'now, please God, you shall have some schooling, child,' and she'd put me to school. But my father were that good in his heart that he couldn't abear to be without us. So, he'd come with a most tremenjous crowd and make such a row at the doors of the houses where we was, that they used to be obligated to have no more to do with us and to give us up to him. And then he took us home and hammered us. Which, you see, Pip," said Joe, pausing in his meditative raking of the fire, and looking at me, "were a drawback on my learning."

"Certainly, poor Joe!"

"Though mind you, Pip," said Joe, with a judicial touch or two of the poker on the top bar, "rendering unto all their doo, and maintaining equal justice betwixt man and man, my father were that good in his heart, don't you see?"

I didn't see; but I didn't say so.

"Well!" Joe pursued, "somebody must keep the pot a-biling, Pip, or the pot won't bile, don't you know?"

I saw that, and said so.

" 'Consequence, my father didn't make objections to my going to work; so I went to work at my present calling, which were his too, if he would have followed it, and I worked tolerable hard, I assure *you*, Pip. In time I were able to keep him, and I kep him till he went off in a purple leptic fit. And **it** were my intentions to have had put upon his tombstone that Whatsume'er the failings on his part, Remember reader he were that good in his hart."

Joe recited this couplet with such manifest pride and careful perspicuity, that I asked him if he had made it himself.

"I made it," said Joe, "my own self. I made it in a moment. It was like striking out a horseshoe complete, in a single blow. I never was so much surprised in all my life — couldn't credit my own ed — to tell you the truth, hardly believed it were *my* own ed. As I was saying, Pip, it were my intentions to have had it cut over him; but poetry costs money, cut it how you will, small or large, and it were not done. Not to mention bearers, all the money that could be spared were wanted for my mother. She were in poor elth, and quite broke. She waren't long of following, poor soul, and her share of peace come round at last."

Joe's blue eyes turned a little watery; he rubbed, first one of them, and then the other, in a most uncongenial and uncomfortable manner, with the round knob on the top of the poker.

"It were but lonesome then," said Joe, "living here alone, and I got acquainted with your sister. Now, Pip"; Joe looked firmly at me, as if he knew I was not going to agree with him; "your sister is a fine figure of a woman."

I could not help looking at the fire, in an obvious state of doubt.

"Whatever family opinions, or whatever the world's opinions, on that subject may be, Pip, your sister is," Joe tapped the top bar with the poker after every word following, "a — fine — figure — of — a — woman!"

I could think of nothing better to say than "I am glad you think so, Joe."

"So am I," returned Joe, catching me up. "*I* am glad I think so, Pip. A little redness, or a little matter of Bone, here or there, what does it signify to Me?"

I sagaciously observed, if it didn't signify to him, to whom did it signify?

"Certainly!" assented Joe. "That's it. You're right, old chap! When I got acquainted with your sister, it were the talk how she was bringing you up by hand. Very kind of her too, all the folks said, and I said, along with all the folks. As to you," Joe pursued, with a countenance expressive of saying something very nasty indeed: "if you could have been aware how small and flabby and mean you was, dear me, you'd have formed the most contemptible opinions of yourself!"

Not exactly relishing this, I said, "Never mind me, Joe."

"But I did mind you, Pip. And when I married your sister, I said, 'Bring the poor little child. There's room for him at the forge.' And now when you take me in hand for learning, Mrs. Joe mustn't see too much of what we are up to. It must be done, as I may say, on the sly. Well you see, Pip, here we are. That's about where it lights — here we are. And we are ever the best friends; ain't us?"

PIP AT MR. PUMBLECHOOK'S

THE first time Pip was away from home was when he went to Mr. Pumblechook's. Mr. Pumblechook lived in a near-by town, where he kept a seed-store in the High Street. He was a big, solemn-looking man and he had an idea that small boys ought to be instructed at all hours. He thought it was good for them. So he kept at mental arithmetic all the time, firing one question after another at poor Pip. When he got up in the morning, Pip said politely, "Good morning, Mr. Pumblechook."

Mr. Pumblechook answered, "Boy, what is seven times nine?" At the breakfast-table he would say, "Seven? and four? and eight? and six? and two? and ten?" All the time Mr. Pumblechook was eating bacon and hot rolls, while Pip was scared for fear he couldn't answer the next question. The hardest thing was to remember about shillings and pence. Mr. Pumblechook would begin with twelve pence make one shilling, and keep on to forty pence make three and four pence. No wonder that Pip was glad to get back to the blacksmith-shop!

DAVID COPPERFIELD

IV

DAVID COPPERFIELD

DICKENS makes David Copperfield tell the story of his life. He begins at the beginning and tells everything that happened to him as a boy, the places where he lived, and the people whom he met. There are few persons whom we can know as thoroughly as David Copperfield. It is all the more lifelike because many of the scenes are taken from the life of Dickens himself.

David's father had died and his mother had married again. His stepfather, Mr. Murdstone, a gentleman with very black hair and whiskers, was all that a stepfather ought not to be, so that David was happiest when he was away from home.

Happily he had a nurse, who was big and good-natured and really loved David. Her name was Clara Peggotty, but they always called her Peggotty. Her home was in a town by the sea. Mr. Peggotty and his nephew Ham and a despondent old lady named Mrs. Gummidge lived in a houseboat on the shore. David was about seven years old when he went with Clara on a carrier's cart to visit the Peggottys.

Ham met them as they got off the cart. He was a great big fellow, six feet tall, and he carried David's box under his arm, while Peggotty trudged along through the sand at his side. There was a fishy smell about everything. There were boats and fishermen's nets scattered about, and an air of pleasant disorder. Everybody seemed to have all the time there was in the world, and nobody was hurried. Evidently Yarmouth was a very pleasant place for a boy on his vacation. There was plenty of room to play in, and no Mr. Murdstone to make him afraid.

"Yon's our house, Master Davy," said Ham.

David looked out and saw a barge high and dry on the beach, with a snug little house built upon it. There was a stovepipe out of which the smoke was coming. When they came up, they found everything was as pleasant as could be. There was a door on one side and tiny little windows. On the mantelpiece was a Dutch clock, and the table had all the tea-things on it.

Peggotty opened a door to show David his bedroom. It was in the stern of the boat where the rudder used to be. There was a little window and a little looking-glass framed with oyster-shells and a tiny bed, and there was a blue mug filled with fresh seaweed.

Pretty soon Mr. Peggotty, Peggotty's older brother and the master of the house, came in. "Glad to see you, sir," said Mr. Peggotty. "How's your ma? Did you leave her pretty jolly?"

David gave him to understand that she was as jolly as could be wished.

"Well," said Mr. Peggotty, "if you can make out here for a fortnut, 'long with her," pointing to his sister, "and Ham, and little Em'ly, we shall be proud of your company."

When I spoke of the people who lived on the old boat, I

had forgotten to mention little Em'ly, who turned out to be the most important member of the family in David's eyes. She was a very pretty little girl, who wore a necklace of blue beads, and thought that she would like to be a lady and marry a prince, or even an earl.

"If I was ever a lady," said Em'ly, "I'd give Uncle Dan," that was Mr. Peggotty, "a sky-blue coat with diamond buttons, nankeen trousers, a red velvet waistcoat, a cocked hat, a large gold watch, a silver pipe, and a box of money."

David thought that was very fine, though it was easier for him to think of Em'ly as dressed like a princess in the fairy books than it was to think of big Mr. Peggotty walking about in a red velvet waistcoat and a cocked hat. As for little Em'ly marrying a prince, that seemed all right if David could be the prince.

All of the Peggotty family were so healthy and cheerful that even Mrs. Gummidge, who lived with them, could not make them unhappy. Mrs. Gummidge was a person who felt that it was necessary to have some one to pity, and as she couldn't pity the Peggottys she got into the habit of pitying herself. She would sit by the fire, and take out an old black handkerchief, and wipe her eyes, and tell her troubles, and then tell how wrong it was in her to tell them.

Mr. Peggotty had just come in from his work, having stopped a few moments at the public house, which was called The Willing Mind. Mrs. Gummidge was wiping her eyes.

"What's amiss, dame?" said Mr. Peggotty.

"Nothing," returned Mrs. Gummidge. "You've come from The Willing Mind, Dan'l?"

"Why yes, I've took a short spell at The Willing Mind to-night," said Mr. Peggotty.

"I'm sorry I should have drove you there."

"Drive! I don't want no driving," returned Mr. Peggotty. "I only go too ready."

"Very ready," said Mrs. Gummidge. "I am sorry that it should be along of me that you're so ready."

"Along of you! It ain't along of you! Don't you believe a bit of it."

"Yes, it is," cried Mrs. Gummidge. "I know what I am. I know I'm a lone lorn creetur', and not only that everythink goes contrairy with me, but that I go contrairy with everybody. Yes, I feel more than other people do, and I know it more. It's my misfortune. I feel my troubles, and they make me contrairy. I wish I didn't feel 'em, but I do. I wish I could be hardened to 'em, but I ain't. I make the house uncomfortable. I don't wonder at it. It's far from right. It ain't a fit return. I'm a lone lorn creetur, I'd better not make myself contrairy here. If things must go contrairy with me, and I must go contrairy with myself, let me go away."

But Mrs. Gummidge had no idea of going away to the poorhouse, as she always threatened; and the Peggottys had no idea of letting her leave their cheerful little home. It was Mrs. Gummidge's way of carrying on conversation, and they had got used to it.

The delightful visit to Yarmouth came to an end, and

DAVID COPPERFIELD

after a time Mr. Murdstone sent David to a school near London. We can see the shy little boy starting off for his first journey alone in the big world. The first part of the journey was easy, because it was in a carrier's cart and the driver was a nice Mr. Barkis, who was in love with Peggotty and liked to talk about her in a very mysterious way, and gave David a message to her, saying that "Barkis is willin'."

David tells of his conversation with Barkis in the cart. He first looked at the purse which his mother had given him.

.   .   .   .

It was a stiff leather purse, with a snap, and had three bright shillings in it, which Peggotty had evidently polished up with whitening for my greater delight. But its most precious contents were two half-crowns folded together in a bit of paper, on which was written, in my mother's hand: "For Davy. With my love." I was so overcome by this that I asked the carrier to be so good as reach me my pocket-handkerchief again; but he said he thought I had better do without it; and I thought I really had; so I wiped my eyes on my sleeve and stopped myself.

For good, too; though, in consequence of my previous emotions, I was still occasionally seized with a stormy sob. After we had jogged on for some little time, I asked the carrier if he was going all the way.

"All the way where?" inquired the carrier.

"There," I said.

"Where's there?" inquired the carrier.

"Near London," I said.

[33]

"Why that horse," said the carrier, jerking the rein to point him out, "would be deader than pork afore he got over half the ground."

"Are you only going to Yarmouth, then?" I asked.

"That's about it," said the carrier. "And there I shall take you to the stage-cutch, and the stage-cutch that'll take you to — wherever it is."

As this was a great deal for the carrier (whose name was Mr. Barkis) to say — he being, as I observed in a former chapter, of a phlegmatic temperament, and not at all conversational — I offered him a cake as a mark of attention, which he ate at one gulp, exactly like an elephant, and which made no more impression on his big face than it would have done on an elephant's.

"Did *she* make 'em, now?" said Mr. Barkis, always leaning forward, in his slouching way, on the footboard of the cart with an arm on each knee.

"Peggotty, do you mean, sir?"

"Ah!" said Mr. Barkis. "Her."

"Yes. She makes all our pastry, and does all our cooking."

"Do she though?" said Mr. Barkis.

He made up his mouth as if to whistle, but he didn't whistle. He sat looking at the horse's ears, as if he saw something new there; and sat so, for a considerable time. By-and-by, he said:

"No sweethearts, I b'lieve?"

"Sweetmeats did you say, Mr. Barkis?" For I thought

he wanted something else to eat, and had pointedly alluded to that description of refreshment.

"Hearts," said Mr. Barkis. "Sweethearts; no person walks with her!"

"With Peggotty?"

"Ah!" he said. "Her."

"Oh, no. She never had a sweetheart."

"Didn't she though!" said Mr. Barkis.

Again he made up his mouth to whistle, and again he didn't whistle, but sat looking at the horse's ears.

"So she makes," said Mr. Barkis, after a long interval of reflection, "all the apple parsties, and doos all the cooking, do she?"

I replied that such was the fact.

"Well. I'll tell you what," said Mr. Barkis. "P'raps you might be writin' to her?"

"I shall certainly write to her," I rejoined.

"Ah!" he said, slowly turning his eyes towards me. "Well! If you was writin' to her, p'raps you'd recollect to say that Barkis was willin'; would you?"

"That Barkis is willing," I repeated, innocently. "Is that all the message?"

"Ye-es," he said, considering. "Ye-es. Barkis is willin'."

"But you will be at Blunderstone again to-morrow, Mr. Barkis," I said, faltering a little at the idea of my being far away from it then, "and could give your own message so much better."

As he repudiated this suggestion, however, with a jerk of his head, and once more confirmed his previous request by saying, with profound gravity, "Barkis is willin'. That's the message," I readily undertook its transmission. While I was waiting for the coach in the hotel at Yarmouth that very afternoon, I procured a sheet of paper and an inkstand, and wrote a note to Peggotty, which ran thus: "My dear Peggotty. I have come here safe. Barkis is willing. My love to mama. Yours affectionately. P. S. He says he particularly wants you to know — *Barkis is willing.*"

When I had taken this commission on myself prospectively, Mr. Barkis relapsed into perfect silence; and I, feeling quite worn out by all that had happened lately, lay down on a sack in the cart and fell asleep.

It was in the inn at Yarmouth that David fell in with a jolly waiter who ate up his dinner for him. David was very much afraid of doing something which he ought not to do. Everything seemed so big and strange.

THE LITTLE BOY AND THE HUNGRY WAITER

THE waiter brought me some chops, and vegetables, and took the covers off in such a bouncing manner that I was afraid I must have given him some offence. But he greatly relieved my mind by putting a chair for me at the table, and saying, very affably, "Now. six-foot! come on!"

I thanked him, and took my seat at the board; but found

LITTLE EM'LY

it extremely difficult to handle my knife and fork with anything like dexterity, or to avoid splashing myself with the gravy, while he was standing opposite, staring so hard, and making me blush in the most dreadful manner every time I caught his eye. After watching me into the second chop, he said:

"There's half a pint of ale for you. Will you have it now?"

I thanked him and said "Yes." Upon which he poured it out of a jug into a large tumbler, and held it up against the light, and made it look beautiful.

"My eye!" he said. "It seems a good deal, don't it?"

"It does seem a good deal," I answered with a smile. For it was quite delightful to me to find him so pleasant. He was a twinkling-eyed, pimple-faced man, with his hair standing upright all over his head; and as he stood with one arm akimbo, holding up the glass to the light with the other hand, he looked quite friendly.

"There was a gentleman here, yesterday," he said, "a stout gentleman, by the name of Topsawyer — perhaps you know him!"

"No," I said, "I don't think ——"

"In breeches and gaiters, broad-brimmed hat, gray coat, speckled choker," said the waiter.

"No," I said bashfully, "I haven't the pleasure ——"

"He came in here," said the waiter, looking at the light through the tumbler, "ordered a glass of this ale — *would* order it — I told him not — drank it, and fell dead. It was too old for him. It oughtn't to be drawn; that's the fact."

I was very much shocked to hear of this melancholy accident, and said I thought I had better have some water.

"Why you see," said the waiter, still looking at the light through the tumbler, with one of his eyes shut up, "our people don't like things being ordered and left. It offends 'em. But *I'll* drink it, if you like. I'm used to it, and use is everything. I don't think it'll hurt me, if I throw my head back, and take it off quick. Shall I?"

I replied that he would much oblige me by drinking it, if he thought he could do it safely, but by no means otherwise. When he did throw his head back, and take it off quickly, I had a horrible fear, I confess, of seeing him meet the fate of the lamented Mr. Topsawyer, and fall lifeless on the carpet. But it didn't hurt him. On the contrary, I thought he seemed the fresher for it.

"What have we got here?" he said, putting a fork into my dish. "Not chops?"

"Chops," I said.

"Lord bless my soul!" he exclaimed. "I didn't know they were chops. Why, a chop's the very thing to take off the bad effects of that beer! Ain't it lucky?"

So he took a chop by the bone in one hand, and a potato in the other, and ate away with a very good appetite, to my extreme satisfaction. He afterwards took another chop, and another potato; and after that another chop and another potato. When he had done, he brought me a pudding, and having set it before me, seemed to ruminate, and to become absent in his mind for some moments.

"How's the pie?" he said, rousing himself.

DAVID COPPERFIELD

"It's a pudding," I made answer.

"Pudding!" he exclaimed. "Why, bless me, so it is! What!" looking at it nearer. "You don't mean to say it's a batter-pudding!"

"Yes, it is indeed."

"Why, a batter-pudding," he said, taking up a table-spoon, "is my favorite pudding! Ain't that lucky? Come on, little 'un, and let's see who'll get most."

The waiter certainly got most. He entreated me more than once to come in and win, but what with his tablespoon to my teaspoon, his despatch to my despatch, and his appe-tite to my appetite, I was left far behind at the first mouthful, and had no chance with him. I never saw any one enjoy a pudding so much, I think; and he laughed, when it was all gone, as if his enjoyment of it lasted still.

Finding him so very friendly and companionable, it was then that I asked for the pen and ink and paper to write to Peggotty. He not only brought it immediately, but was good enough to look over me while I wrote the letter. When I had finished it, he asked me where I was going to school.

I said, "Near London," which was all I knew.

"Oh! my eye!" he said, looking very low-spirited. "I am sorry for that."

"Why?" I asked him.

"Oh, Lord!" he said, shaking his head, "that's the school where they broke the boy's ribs — two ribs — a little boy he was. I should say he was — let me see — how old are you, about?"

I told him between eight and nine.

"That's just his age," he said. "He was eight years and six months old when they broke his first rib; eight years and eight months old when they broke his second, and did for him."

I could not disguise from myself, or from the waiter, that this was an uncomfortable coincidence, and inquired how it was done. His answer was not cheering to my spirits, for it consisted of two dismal words: "With whopping."

The blowing of the coach horn in the yard was a seasonable diversion, which made me get up and hesitatingly inquire, in the mingled pride and diffidence of having a purse (which I took out of my pocket), if there were anything to pay.

"There's a sheet of letter-paper," he returned. "Did you ever buy a sheet of letter-paper?"

I could not remember that I ever had.

"It's dear," he said, "on account of the duty. Threepence. That's the way we're taxed in this country. There's nothing else, except the waiter. Never mind the ink. *I* lose by that."

"What should you — what should I — how much ought I to — what would it be right to pay the waiter, if you please?" I stammered, blushing.

"If I hadn't a family, and that family hadn't the cowpock," said the waiter, "I wouldn't take a sixpence. If I didn't support an aged pairint and a lovely sister," — here the waiter was greatly agitated — "I wouldn't take a farthing. If I had a good place, and was treated well here, I should beg acceptance of a trifle, instead of taking of it. But I live on broken wittles — and I sleep on the coals" — here the waiter burst into tears.

I was very much concerned for his misfortunes, and felt that any recognition short of ninepence would be mere brutality and hardness of heart. Therefore I gave him one of my three bright shillings, which he received with much humility and veneration, and spun up with his thumb, directly afterwards, to try the goodness of.

WILKINS MICAWBER JUNIOR AND HIS PARENTS

V

WILKINS MICAWBER JUNIOR AND HIS PARENTS

I DO not think that I should devote a chapter in *The Children of Dickens* to Wilkins Micawber Junior if it were not for his parents, who were very amusing persons whom everybody ought to know. Wilkins Micawber Junior never did anything or said anything in particular. He was a child who was seen and not heard. He was always standing around listening to his father and mother, and he had to do a good deal of listening, for they talked incessantly, chiefly about themselves. And then he was always pointed at, when they wanted to tell of their troubles. He was about four years old when we first see him pointed at, and he had a sister who was a year younger. Then there were the twins, who were always in their mother's arms.

The Micawbers lived in a shabby house on Windsor Terrace, where they took David Copperfield to board. That is, they lived there when Mr. Micawber was not in the Debtors' Prison. David Copperfield found it a great relief to get away from the company of Mealy Potatoes, the boy he worked with in Murdstone's establishment, and get into the friendly company of the Micawbers.

The Micawbers were always in trouble, but they enjoyed their troubles and were willing to share their enjoyment with

[45]

anybody who would listen to them. Though David Copperfield was only twelve years old, Mr. Micawber always treated him as an equal, and used the largest words he could think of. David liked to be talked to that way, so they became great friends. Wilkins Micawber Junior stood by and listened, and thought his father was the most wonderful talker in the world. When he grew up and had a family to support and couldn't do it, he would talk that way.

David Copperfield tells how he first met Mr. Micawber at the office of Murdstone and Grinby and went home with him to Windsor Terrace.

.   .   .   .

The counting-house clock was at half-past twelve, and there was general preparation for going to dinner, when Mr. Quinion tapped at the counting-house window, and beckoned to me to go in. I went in, and found there a stoutish, middle-aged person, in a brown surtout and black tights and shoes, with no more hair upon his head (which was a large one, and very shining) than there is upon an egg, and with a very extensive face, which he turned full upon me. His clothes were shabby, but he had an imposing shirt-collar on. He carried a jaunty sort of a stick, with a large pair of rusty tassels to it; and a quizzing-glass hung outside his coat, — for ornament, I afterwards found, as he very seldom looked through it, and couldn't see anything when he did.

"This," said Mr. Quinion, in allusion to myself, "is he."

"This," said the stranger, with a certain condescending roll in his voice, and a certain indescribable air of doing something genteel, which impressed me very much "is Master Copperfield. I hope I see you well, Sir?"

I said I was very well, and hoped he was. I was sufficiently ill at ease, Heaven knows; but it was not in my nature to complain much at that time of my life, so I said I was very well, and hoped he was.

"I am," said the stranger, "thank Heaven, quite well. I have received a letter from Mr. Murdstone, in which he mentions that he would desire me to receive into an apartment in the rear of my house, which is at present unoccupied — and is, in short, to be let as a — in short," said the stranger, with a smile and in a burst of confidence, "as a bedroom — the young beginner whom I have now the pleasure to — " and the stranger waved his hand, and settled his chin in his shirt-collar.

"This is Mr. Micawber," said Mr. Quinion to me.

"Ahem!" said the stranger, "that is my name."

"Mr. Micawber," said Mr. Quinion, "is known to Mr. Murdstone. He takes orders for us on commission, when he can get any. He has been written to by Mr. Murdstone, on the subject of your lodgings, and he will receive you as a lodger."

"My address," said Mr. Micawber, "is Windsor Terrace, City Road. I — in short," said Mr. Micawber, with the same genteel air, and in another burst of confidence — "I live there."

I made him a bow.

"Under the impression," said Mr. Micawber, "that your

peregrinations in this metropolis have not as yet been extensive, and that you might have some difficulty in penetrating
the arcana of the Modern Babylon in the direction of the
City Road — in short," said Mr. Micawber, in another burst
of confidence, "that you might lose yourself — I shall be happy
to call this evening, and install you in the knowledge of the
nearest way."

I thanked him with all my heart, for it was friendly in
him to offer to take that trouble.

"At what hour," said Mr. Micawber, "shall I —— "

"At about eight," said Mr. Quinion.

"At about eight," said Mr. Micawber. "I beg to wish
you good day, Mr. Quinion. I will intrude no longer."

So he put on his hat, and went out with his cane under
his arm: very upright, and humming a tune when he was
clear of the counting-house.

Mr. Quinion then formally engaged me to be as useful as
I could in the warehouse of Murdstone and Grinby, at a
salary, I think, of six shillings a week. I am not clear whether
it was six or seven. I am inclined to believe, from my uncertainty on this head, that it was six at first and seven afterwards. He paid me a week down (from his own pocket, I
believe), and I gave Mealy sixpence out of it to get my trunk
carried to Windsor Terrace at night: it being too heavy for
my strength, small as it was. I paid sixpence more for my
dinner, which was a meat pie and a turn at a neighboring
pump; and passed the hour which was allowed for that meal,
in walking about the streets.

WILKINS MICAWBER JUNIOR

At the appointed time in the evening, Mr. Micawber reappeared. I washed my hands and face, to do the greater honor to his gentility, and we walked to our house, as I suppose I must now call it, together; Mr. Micawber impressing the names of streets, and the shapes of corner houses upon me, as we went along, that I might find my way back, easily, in the morning.

Arrived at his house in Windsor Terrace (which I noticed was shabby like himself, but also, like himself, made all the show it could), he presented me to Mrs. Micawber, a thin and faded lady, not at all young, who was sitting in the parlor (the first floor was altogether unfurnished, and the blinds were kept down to delude the neighbors), with a baby at her breast. This baby was one of twins; and I may remark here that I hardly ever, in all my experience of the family, saw both the twins detached from Mrs. Micawber at the same time. One of them was always taking refreshment.

There were two other children; Master Micawber, aged about four, and Miss Micawber, aged about three. These, and a dark-complexioned young woman, with a habit of snorting, who was servant to the family, and informed me, before half-an-hour had expired, that she was "a Orfling," and came from St. Luke's workhouse, in the neighborhood, completed the establishment. My room was at the top of the house, at the back: a close chamber; stencilled all over with an ornament which my young imagination represented as a blue muffin; and very scantily furnished.

"I never thought," said Mrs. Micawber, when she came

up, twin and all, to show me the apartment, and sat down
to take breath, "before I was married, when I lived with
papa and mama, that I should ever find it necessary to take
a lodger. But Mr. Micawber being in difficulties, all consider-
ations of private feelings must give way."

I said: "Yes, ma'am."

"Mr. Micawber's difficulties are almost overwhelming
just at present," said Mrs. Micawber, "and whether it is possible to bring him through them, I don't know. When I lived
at home with papa and mama, I really should have hardly
understood what the word meant, in the sense in which I
now employ it, but experientia does it — as papa used to
say."

I cannot satisfy myself whether she told me that Mr.
Micawber had been an officer in the Marines, or whether I
have imagined it. I only know that I believe to this hour
that he *was* in the Marines once upon a time, without knowing
why. He was a sort of town traveller for a number of mis-
cellaneous houses, now; but made little or nothing of it, I am
afraid.

"If Mr. Micawber's creditors *will not* give him time,"
said Mrs. Micawber, "they must take the consequences; and
the sooner they bring it to an issue the better. Blood cannot be obtained from a stone, neither can anything on account
be obtained at present (not to mention law expenses) from
Mr. Micawber."

I never can quite understand whether my precocious
self-dependence confused Mrs. Micawber in reference to my

age, or whether she was so full of the subject that she would have talked about it to the very twins if there had been nobody else to communicate with, but this was the strain in which she began, and she went on accordingly all the time I knew her.

Poor Mrs. Micawber! She said she had tried to exert herself; and so, I have no doubt, she had. The centre of the street door was perfectly covered with a great brass plate, on which was engraved, "Mrs. Micawber's Boarding Establishment for Young Ladies," but I never found that any young lady had ever been to school there; or that any young lady ever came, or proposed to come; or that the least preparation was ever made to receive any young lady. The only visitors I ever saw or heard of, were creditors. *They* used to come at all hours, and some of them were quite ferocious. One dirty-faced man, I think he was a bootmaker, used to edge himself into the passage as early as seven o'clock in the morning, and call up the stairs to Mr. Micawber — "Come! You ain't out yet, you know. Pay us, will you? Don't hide, you know; that's mean. I wouldn't be mean if I was you. Pay us, will you? You just pay us, d'ye hear? Come!" Receiving no answer to these taunts, he would mount in his wrath to the words "swindlers" and "robbers"; and these being ineffectual, too, would sometimes go to the extremity of crossing the street, and roaring up at the windows of the second floor, where he knew Mr. Micawber was. At these times, Mr. Micawber would be transported with grief and mortification, even to the length (as I was once made aware by a scream from his wife) of making motions at himself with a razor; but within half an hour afterwards, he would polish up his shoes with extraordinary pains, and go out, humming a tune with a greater air of gentility than ever. Mrs. Micawber was quite as elastic. I have known her to be thrown into fainting fits by the King's taxes at three o'clock, and to eat lamb chops, breaded, and drink warm ale (paid for with two teaspoons that had gone to the pawnbroker's) at four. On one occasion, when an execution had just been put in, coming home through some chance as early as six o'clock, I saw her lying (of course with a twin) under the grate in a swoon, with her hair all torn about her face; but I never knew her more cheerful than she was, that very same night, over a veal cutlet before the kitchen fire, telling me stories about her papa and mama, and the company they used to keep.

.   .   .   .

The Micawbers' affairs went from bad to worse, and Mrs. Micawber called David into consultation.

.   .   .   .

"Master Copperfield," said Mrs. Micawber, "I make no stranger of you, and therefore do not hesitate to say that Mr. Micawber's difficulties are coming to a crisis."

It made me very miserable to hear it, and I looked at Mrs. Micawber's red eyes with the utmost sympathy.

"With the exception of the heel of a Dutch cheese — which is not adapted to the wants of a young family," said Mrs. Micawber — "there is really not a scrap of anything in the larder. I was accustomed to speak of the larder when I lived with papa and mama, and I use the word almost unconsciously. What I mean to express is, that there is nothing to eat in the house."

"Dear me!" I said, in great concern.

I had two or three shillings of my week's money in my pocket — from which I presume that it must have been on a Wednesday night when we held this conversation — and I hastily produced them, and with heartfelt emotion begged Mrs. Micawber to accept of them as a loan. But that lady, kissing me, and making me put them back in my pocket, replied that she couldn't think of it.

"No, my dear Master Copperfield," said she, "far be it from my thoughts! But you have a discretion beyond your years, and can render me another kind of service, if you will; and a service I will thankfully accept of."

I begged Mrs. Micawber to name it.

"I have parted with the plate myself," said Mrs. Micawber. "Six tea, two salt, and a pair of sugars, I have at different times borrowed money on, in secret, with my own hands. But the twins are a great tie; and to me, with my recollections of papa and mama, these transactions are very painful. There are still a few trifles that we could part with. Mr. Micawber's feelings would never allow *him* to dispose of them; and Clickett" — this was the girl from the workhouse — "being of a vulgar mind, would take painful liberties if so much confidence was reposed in her. Master Copperfield, if I might ask you —— "

I understood Mrs. Micawber now, and begged her to make

use of me to any extent. I began to dispose of the more portable articles of property that very evening; and went out on a similar expedition almost every morning, before I went to Murdstone and Grinby's.

.   .   .   .

At last Mr. Micawber's affairs got into such a bad state that he had to leave London. David tells of the parting.

.   .   .   .

I passed my evenings with Mr. and Mrs. Micawber, during the remaining term of our residence under the same roof; and I think we became fonder of one another as the time went on. On the last Sunday, they invited me to dinner; and we had a loin of pork and apple sauce, and a pudding. I had bought a spotted wooden horse overnight as a parting gift to little Wilkins Micawber — that was the boy — and a doll for little Emma. I had also bestowed a shilling on the Orfling, who was about to be disbanded.

We had a very pleasant day, though we were all in a tender state about our approaching separation.

"I shall never, Master Copperfield," said Mrs. Micawber, "revert to the period when Mr. Micawber was in difficulties without thinking of you. Your conduct has always been of the most delicate and obliging description. You have never been a lodger. You have been a friend."

"My dear," said Mr. Micawber, "Copperfield," for so he had been accustomed to call me of late, "has a heart to feel for the distresses of his fellow-creatures when they are behind a cloud, and a head to plan, and a hand to — in short, a general ability to dispose of such available property as could be made away with."

I expressed my sense of this commendation, and said I was very sorry we were going to lose one another.

"My dear young friend," said Mr. Micawber, "I am older than you; a man of some experience in life, and — and of some experience, in short, in difficulties, generally speaking. At present, and until something turns up (which I am, I may say, hourly expecting), I have nothing to bestow but advice. Still, my advice is so far worth taking, that — in short, that I have never taken it myself, and am the" — here Mr. Micawber, who had been beaming and smiling, all over his head and face, up to the present moment, checked himself and frowned — "the miserable wretch you behold."

"My dear Micawber!" urged his wife.

"I say," returned Mr. Micawber, quite forgetting himself, and smiling again, "the miserable wretch you behold. My advice is, never do to-morrow what you can do to-day. Procrastination is the thief of time. Collar him!"

"My poor papa's maxim," Mrs. Micawber observed.

"My dear," said Mr. Micawber, "your papa was very well in his way, and Heaven forbid that I should disparage him. Take him for all in all, we ne'er shall — in short, make the acquaintance, probably, of anybody else possessing, at his time of life, the same legs for gaiters, and able to read the same description of print without spectacles. But he applied that maxim to our marriage, my dear; and that was so far

[55]

prematurely entered into, in consequence, that I never recovered the expense."

Mr. Micawber looked aside at Mrs. Micawber, and added: "Not that I am sorry for it. Quite the contrary, my love." After which he was grave for a minute or so.

"My other piece of advice, Copperfield," said Mr. Micawber, "you know. Annual income twenty pounds, annual expenditure nineteen ought and six, result happiness. Annual income twenty pounds, annual expenditure twenty pounds ought and six, result misery. The blossom is blighted, the leaf is withered, the God of day goes down upon the dreary scene, and — and in short you are for ever floored. As I am!"

To make his example the more impressive, Mr. Micawber drank a glass of punch with an air of great enjoyment and satisfaction and whistled the College Hornpipe.

I did not fail to assure him that I would store these precepts in my mind, though indeed I had no need to do so, for, at the time, they affected me visibly. Next morning I met the whole family at the coach office, and saw them, with a desolate heart, take their places outside, at the back.

"Master Copperfield," said Mrs. Micawber, "God bless you! I never can forget all that, you know, and I never would if I could."

"Copperfield," said Mr. Micawber, "farewell. Every happiness and prosperity. If, in the progress of revolving years, I could persuade myself that my blighted destiny had been a warning to you, I should feel that I had not occupied another man's place in existence altogether in vain. In case of anything turning up (of which I am rather confident), I shall be extremely happy if it should be in my power to improve your prospects."

I think, as Mrs. Micawber sat at the back of the coach, with the children, and I stood in the road looking wistfully at them, a mist cleared from her eyes, and she saw what a little creature I really was. I think so, because she beckoned to me to climb up, with quite a new and motherly expression in her face, and put her arm round my neck, and gave me just such a kiss as she might have given to her own boy. I had barely time to get down again before the coach started, and I could hardly see the family for the handkerchiefs they waved. It was gone in a minute.

ON THE ROAD TO DOVER

VI

ON THE ROAD TO DOVER

AFTER his friends the Micawbers had left London David Copperfield was very lonesome and decided to set out on a journey and find his aunt, Miss Betsy Trotwood. He had a box which he intended to send to the coach office in Dover, and he had a half-guinea in his pocket.

Unfortunately he met a long-legged young man who was driving a donkey cart, who robbed him of his box and his money. David followed the young man as long as he could and then sat down by the side of the road. He searched his pockets and found only three halfpence. But his experience with Mr. Micawber had taught him that he could borrow money at a pawn-shop. He tells the story of what happened.

. . . .

I went to the next street and took off my waistcoat, rolled it neatly under my arm, and came to the shop door. Mr. Dolloby was the name over the door.

Mr. Dolloby took the waistcoat, spread it on the counter, held it up against the light, and at last said:

"What do you call a price for this here little weskit?"

"Oh, you know best, sir," I returned modestly.

"I can't be buyer and seller too," said Mr. Dolloby. "Put a price on this little weskit."

"Would eighteen pence be — " I hinted.

Mr. Dolloby rolled it up again and gave it back to me.

"I should rob my family if I was to offer ninepence for it."

This was a disagreeable way of putting it, for I did not want to ask Mr. Dolloby to rob his family on my account. I would have to make the best of my way to Dover in a shirt and a pair of trousers.

That night I lay behind a wall. Never shall I forget the feeling of loneliness as I lay down without a roof over my head. But soon I was asleep, and slept until the warm beams of the sun awoke me.

The next day was Sunday. In due time I heard the church bells ringing. I passed a church or two where the congregations were inside. The peace and rest of Sunday morning were on everything but me. I felt quite wicked in my dust and dirt, and my tangled hair.

I got that Sunday to the bridge at Rochester footsore and tired, and eating food that I had bought for supper. I toiled on to Chatham and crept upon a sort of grass-grown battery, where a sentry was walking to and fro. Here I lay near a cannon, happy in the society of the sentry's footsteps, though he knew nothing of my being there.

Very stiff and sore of foot I was in the morning, and quite dazed by the beating of drums and marching of troops, which seemed to hem me in on every side when I went down toward the long, narrow street. Feeling that I could go but a very little way that day, if I were to reserve my strength for getting to my journey's end, I resolved to make the sale of my jacket its principal business. Accordingly, I took the jacket off, that I might learn to do without it; and carrying it under my arm, began a tour of inspection of the various slop-shops.

It was a likely place to sell a jacket in; for the dealers in second-hand clothes were numerous, and were, generally speaking, on the lookout for customers at their shop doors. But, as most of them had, hanging up among their stock, an officer's coat or two, epaulets and all, I was rendered timid by the costly nature of their dealings, and walked about for a long time without offering my merchandise to any one.

This modesty of mine directed my attention to the marine-store shops, and such shops as Mr. Dolloby's, in preference to the regular dealers. At last I found one that I thought looked promising, at the corner of a dirty lane, ending in an inclosure full of stinging nettles, against the palings of which some second-hand sailors' clothes, that seemed to have overflown the shop, were fluttering among some cots, and rusty guns, and oilskin hats, and certain trays full of so many old rusty keys of so many sizes that they seemed various enough to open all the doors in the world.

Into this shop, which was low and small, and which was darkened rather than lighted by a little window, overhung with clothes, and was descended into by some steps, I went with a palpitating heart; which was not relieved when an ugly old man, with the lower part of his face all covered with a stubby gray beard, rushed out of a dirty den behind it, and seized me by the hair of my head. He was a dreadful old man to look at, in a filthy flannel waistcoat, and smelling terribly of rum. His bedstead, covered with a tumbled and ragged piece of patchwork, was in the den he had come from, where another little window showed a prospect of more stinging nettles, and a lame donkey.

"Oh, what do you want?" grinned this old man in a fierce, monotonous whine. "Oh, my eyes and limbs, what do you want? Oh, my lungs and liver, what do you want? Oh, goroo, goroo!"

I was so much dismayed by these words, and particularly by the repetition of the last unknown one, which was a kind of rattle in his throat, that I could make no answer; whereupon the old man, still holding me by the hair, repeated:

"Oh, what do you want? Oh, my lungs and liver, what do you want?"

"I want to know," I said trembling, "if you would buy a jacket?"

"Oh, let's see the jacket. Bring the jacket out."

With that he took his trembling hands, which were like the claws of a bird, out of my hair.

"How much for the jacket?" cried the old man. "Oh, goroo, how much for the jacket?"

"Half a crown," I answered.

"Oh, my lungs and liver, no. Oh, my eyes, no. Eighteen pence. Goroo."

Every time he said goroo his eyes seemed in danger of popping out of his head.

"Well," said I, "I'll take eighteen pence."

"Oh, my liver," cried the old man, throwing the jacket

on the shelf. "Get out of the shop. Don't ask for money, make it an exchange."

He made many attempts to make me consent to an exchange, at one time coming out with a fishing-rod, at another with a fiddle, at another with a cocked hat, at another with a flute. But I wanted the money to buy food. At last he began to pay me in halfpence at a time, and was full two hours getting by easy stages to a shilling.

My bed that night was under a haystack, where I rested comfortably, after having washed my blistered feet in a stream. When I took the road again next morning it was through hop fields and orchards. The orchards were ruddy with bright apples, and in a few places the hop-pickers were already at work. I thought it all extremely beautiful, and I would have enjoyed it if it had not been for the people I met on the road.

The trampers were worse than ever that day, and inspired me with a dread that is yet quite fresh in my mind. Some of them were most ferocious looking ruffians, who stared at me as I went by; and stopped, perhaps, and called after me to come back and speak to them; and when I took to my heels, stoned me. I recollect one young fellow — a tinker, I suppose, from his wallet and brazier — who had a woman with him, and who faced about and stared at me thus; and then roared at me in such a tremendous voice to come back, that I halted and looked round.

"Come here, when you're called," said the tinker, "or I'll rip your young body open."

I thought it best to go back. As I drew nearer to them, trying to propitiate the tinker by my looks, I observed that the woman had a black eye.

"Where are you going?" said the tinker, gripping the bosom of my shirt with his blackened hand.

"I'm going to Dover," I said.

"Where do you come from?" asked the tinker, giving his hand another turn in my shirt to hold me more securely.

"I come from London," I said.

"What lay are you upon?" asked the tinker. "Are you a prig?"

"N—no," I said.

"Ain't you! If you make a brag of your honesty to me," said the tinker, "I'll knock your brains out."

With his disengaged hand he made a menace of striking me, and then looked at me from head to foot.

"Have you got the price of a pint of beer about you?" said the tinker. "If you have, out with it, afore I take it away."

I should certainly have produced it, but that I met the woman's look, and saw her very slightly shake her head, and form "No" with her lips.

"I am very poor," I said, attempting to smile, "and have got no money."

"Why, what do you mean?" said the tinker, looking so sternly at me, that I almost feared he saw the money in my pocket.

"Sir!" I stammered.

"What do you mean," said the tinker, "by wearing my

brother's silk handkerchief? Give it over here!" And he had mine off my neck in a moment, and tossed it to the woman.

The woman burst into a fit of laughter, as if she thought this a joke, and tossing it back to me, nodded once, as slightly as before, and made the word "Go!" with her lips.

It was on the sixth day of my flight that I came to my aunt's house. My shoes were by this time in a woeful condition. My hat was crushed and bent. My shirt and trousers were stained with peat, dew, grass, and the Kentish soil on which I had slept. My hair had known no comb or brush since I left London. From head to foot I was powdered with chalk as if I had come out of a lime kiln.

There came out of the house a lady with a handkerchief tied over her cap, a pair of gardening gloves on her hands, and carrying a great knife. I knew her, immediately, to be my Aunt Betsy.

"Go away!" said Miss Betsy, shaking her head. "Go along! No boys here!"

"If you please, ma'am," I began. She started and looked up.

"If you please, aunt."

"Eh!" exclaimed Miss Betsy in a tone of amazement I have never heard approached.

"If you please, aunt, I am your nephew."

"Oh, Lord!" said my aunt, and sat flat down on the garden path.

"I am David Copperfield. I have been very unhappy since my mother died. I was put to work that was not fit for me. It made me run away to you. I was robbed when I set out and have walked all the way and have never slept in a bed since I began the journey."

My aunt got up in a great hurry, collared me and took me into the parlor. Her first proceeding was to unlock a tall cupboard, bring forth several bottles, and pour some of the contents of each into my mouth. I think they must have been taken out at random, for I am sure I tasted aniseed water, anchovy sauce, and salad dressing. Then she put me on the sofa, with a shawl under my head, and, sitting by my side, repeated at intervals, "Mercy on us!"

Then I was given a bath, which was a great comfort. For I began to be sensitive of pains from lying out in the fields. When I had bathed they enrobed me in a shirt and a pair of trousers too big for me, and tied me up in two or three big shawls. What sort of a bundle I looked like I do not know. Feeling very drowsy, I lay down on the sofa and was soon fast asleep.

Then I was put to bed in a pleasant room at the top of the house. It was overlooking the sea, on which the moon was shining. After I had said my prayers and the candle had burned out I sat looking at the moonlight on the water. Then I turned to the white curtained bed. I remember how I thought of all the solitary places under the night sky where I had slept, and I prayed that I might never be houseless any more, and never might forget the houseless.

JOE THE FAT BOY

VII

JOE THE FAT BOY

WHEN we think of famous people, we take for granted that they did something remarkable. But this is not always true. One of the most famous characters of fiction is the Fat Boy in *The Pickwick Papers*. Everybody remembers him. But what did he do to earn his reputation? He did nothing at all but go to sleep under all circumstances. It was his gift.

Joe was the footman, or rather the footboy, of Mr. Wardle, a good-natured gentleman who lived at Dingley Dell. Now four other good-natured gentlemen had started out from London in search of adventures. Their names were Mr. Pickwick, Mr. Snodgrass, Mr. Tupman, and Mr. Winkle. They didn't know where they were going, but that didn't matter. They intended to have a good time and to see the country. When they returned they were sure that they would have something to tell about. So when they came to the pleasant city of Rochester, they were delighted to find that there was to be a great review of the troops. The soldiers were to take part in a mimic battle. Everything was to be like real war, except that nobody was to be hurt. This was just what Mr. Pickwick and his friends wanted to see.

It was all very fine so long as the soldiers were firing in other directions. But it was different when Mr. Pickwick saw the muskets pointed in their direction. This was getting decidedly dangerous.

"What are they doing now?" inquired Mr. Pickwick.

"I rather think," said Mr. Winkle, "that they are going to fire."

"Nonsense," said Mr. Pickwick.

"I — I — really think they are," urged Mr. Snodgrass, somewhat alarmed.

"Impossible," replied Mr. Pickwick. He had hardly uttered the words when the whole half-dozen regiments levelled their muskets at Mr. Pickwick and his friends, and there burst forth the most tremendous discharge. Mr. Pickwick assured his friends that there was no danger.

"But suppose," said Mr. Winkle, "that some of the men should have ball cartridges by mistake. I heard something whistle in the air just now."

"We had better throw ourselves on our faces, hadn't we?" said Mr. Snodgrass.

"No, it's over now," said Mr. Pickwick.

But it wasn't over. A minute after, the order was given to charge with fixed bayonets, and Mr. Pickwick and his friends saw the six regiments charging across the field to the very spot where they were standing.

"Get out of the way!" cried the officers.

"Where are we to go to?" screamed Mr. Pickwick.

There was nothing for Mr. Pickwick and his friends to do but to get out of the way as fast as they could. There was a gentle wind blowing, and it carried Mr. Pickwick's hat across the field. He ran after it as fast as he could, till it went under the wheels of a carriage from which the horses had been taken out. In the carriage was a stout old gentleman in a blue coat and bright buttons, corduroy breeches and top boots, two young ladies in scarfs and feathers, and an aunt. At the back of the carriage was a huge hamper with cold chicken, ham, tongue, and all the materials for a picnic, and on the box sat a very fat and very red-faced boy, sound asleep.

The stout gentleman in the blue coat was Mr. Wardle, who instantly became a warm friend of Mr. Pickwick, and invited him to get into the carriage and have something to eat.

"Come along, sir, pray come up. Joe! That boy has gone to sleep again. Joe, let down the steps." The fat boy rolled slowly off the box, let down the steps, and held the carriage door invitingly open.

"Room for you all, gentlemen." said the stout man. "Joe, make room for one of these gentlemen on the box. Now, sir, come along." And he pulled Mr. Pickwick and Mr. Snodgrass in by main force.

When they were all in the carriage, Mr. Wardle called to Joe, who had again gone to sleep, to prepare for the lunch.

"Now Joe, knives and forks." The knives and forks were handed to the ladies and gentlemen inside.

"Plates, Joe, plates!" But Joe had dropped to sleep again. "Now, Joe, the fowls. Come hand in the eatables!"

There was something in the last words that roused Joe to the greatest activity, for he was always ready to eat.

[73]

"That's right — look sharp. Now the tongue — now the pigeon pie. Take care of the veal and ham — mind the lobsters — take the salad out of the cloth — give me the dressing." The various dishes were placed in everybody's hands and on everybody's knees.

"Now, ain't this capital?" inquired Mr. Wardle.

"Capital!" said Mr. Winkle, who was carving a fowl on the box.

Everybody was eating and talking at the same time, and they felt that they had always known each other. All except Joe, who preferred a nap to conversation.

"Very extraordinary boy, that," said Mr. Pickwick. "Does he always sleep that way?"

"Sleep!" said the old gentleman, "he's always asleep. Goes on errands fast asleep, and snores as he waits at the table."

"How very odd," said Mr. Pickwick.

"Ah! odd indeed," returned the old gentleman; "I'm proud of that boy — wouldn't part with him on any account — he's a natural curiosity! Here, Joe — Joe — take these things away, and open another bottle — d'ye hear?"

The fat boy rose, opened his eyes, swallowed the huge piece of pie he had been in the act of masticating when he last fell asleep, and slowly obeyed his master's orders — gloating languidly over the remains of the feast, as he removed the plates, and deposited them in the hamper. The fresh bottle was produced, and speedily emptied: the hamper was made fast in its old place — the fat boy once more mounted the box — the spectacles and pocket-glass were again adjusted — and the evolutions of the military recommenced. There was a great fizzing and banging of guns, and starting of ladies — and then a mine was sprung, to the gratification of everybody — and when the mine had gone off, the military and the company followed its example, and went off too.

"Now, mind," said the old gentleman, as he shook hands with Mr. Pickwick at the conclusion of a conversation which had been carried on at intervals, during the conclusion of the proceedings — "we shall see you all to-morrow."

"Most certainly," replied Mr. Pickwick.

"You have got the address?"

"Manor Farm, Dingley Dell," said Mr. Pickwick, consulting his pocket-book.

"That's it," said the old gentleman. "I don't let you off, mind, under a week; and undertake that you shall see everything worth seeing. If you've come down for a country life, come to me, and I'll give you plenty of it. Joe — he's gone to sleep again — Joe, help Tom put in the horses."

The horses were put in — the driver mounted — the fat boy clambered up by his side — farewells were exchanged — and the carriage rattled off. As the Pickwickians turned round to take a last glimpse of it, the setting sun cast a rich glow on the faces of their entertainers, and fell upon the form of the fat boy. His head was sunk upon his bosom; and he slumbered again.

[75]

OLIVER TWIST

VIII

OLIVER TWIST

OLIVER TWIST was born in a poorhouse, where his mother died. The superintendent, Mr. Bumble, was a detestable man, who did all that he could to make the paupers in his institution even more unhappy than they were. He fed the boys on very thin gruel and gave them very little of that. One day when he was particularly hungry, Oliver said:

"Please, sir, I want some more."

Every one was horrified, and poor Oliver was beaten and shut up in a little room where he could meditate on his sin. Soon after, he was given into the hands of Mr. Sowerberry, who was as cruel as Mr. Bumble himself. The upshot of it was that Oliver put a crust of bread, a shirt and two pairs of stockings in a bundle, and ran away. Of course, there was only one place to run away to, and that was London.

Oliver had been six days on the London road when he limped into the little town of Barnet. There he met a boy of his own age, who was the queerest-looking creature he had ever seen. His name was Jack Dawkins, but he was known by all the people who knew him as the Artful Dodger. He was a snub-nosed boy with a dirty face. His hat was on one side of his head and was always about to fall off. He wore a ragged coat which was too large for him, and had turned the coat-sleeves back half-way up his arms.

"Hullo, what's the row?" said the Artful Dodger.

"I am very hungry and tired. I have walked a long way. I have been walking seven days."

"Walking for sivin days! Come, you want grub, and you shall have it."

He took Oliver into a little shop and bought some ham and bread, which was quietly devoured.

"Going to London?" said the strange boy.

"Yes."

"Got any lodgings?"

"No."

"Money?"

"No."

The strange boy whistled; and put his hands into his pockets, as far as the big coat-sleeves would let them go.

"Do you live in London?" inquired Oliver.

"Yes, I do, when I'm at home," replied the boy. "I suppose you want some place to sleep in to-night, don't you?"

"Yes, I do," answered Oliver. "I have not slept under a roof since I left the country."

"Don't fret your eyelids on that score," said the boy. "I've got to be in London to-night; and I know a 'spectable old genelman as lives there, wot'll give you lodgings for nothink, and never ask for the change; that is, if any genelman he knows interduces you. And don't he know me? Oh, no! Not in the least! By no means. Certainly not!"

So Oliver Twist went with the Artful Dodger through the narrowest and crookedest streets in London till he came to the house of old Fagin, who kept a school for pickpockets. Every day the boys would be sent out on the streets and would come home at night with pocket-handkerchiefs and purses which they had snatched from people in the crowds.

Five or six boys were in the room, and Fagin was cooking sausages in a frying-pan.

"This is him, Fagin," said the Artful Dodger; "my friend Oliver Twist."

Fagin grinned, and shook hands. "We are glad to see you, Oliver. Dodger, take off the sausages and draw a tub near the fire for Oliver. Ah, you're a-staring at the pocket-handkerchiefs! eh, my dear? We've just looked 'em out, ready for the wash; that's all, Oliver; that's all."

Oliver wondered very much why they had so many hand-kerchiefs. Fagin employed him in picking out the marks in them, and that kept him busy for several days. One day he went out with the Artful Dodger and his friend Charley Bates. Dickens tells the story of their adventure:

The three boys sallied out; the Dodger with his coat-sleeves tucked up, and his hat cocked, as usual; Master Bates sauntering along with his hands in his pockets; and Oliver between them: wondering where they were going: and what branch of manufacture he would be instructed in, first.

The pace at which they went, was such a very lazy, ill-looking saunter, that Oliver soon began to think his companions were going to deceive the old gentleman, by not going to work at all. The Dodger had a vicious propensity, too, of pulling the caps from the heads of small boys and tossing them down areas; while Charley Bates exhibited some very loose notions concerning the rights of property, by pilfering divers apples and onions from the stalls at the kennel sides, and thrusting them into pockets which were so surprisingly capacious, that they seemed to undermine his whole suit of clothes in every direction. These things looked so bad, that Oliver was on the point of declaring his intention of seeking his way back, in the best way he could; when his thoughts were suddenly directed into another channel, by a very mysterious change of behavior on the part of the Dodger.

They were just emerging from a narrow court not far from the open square in Clerkenwell, which is yet called, by some strange perversion of terms, "The Green," when the Dodger made a sudden stop and, laying his finger on his lip, drew his companions back again, with the greatest caution and circumspection.

"What's the matter?" demanded Oliver.

"Hush!" replied the Dodger. "Do you see that old cove at the book-stall?"

"The old gentleman over the way?" said Oliver. "Yes, I see him."

"He'll do," said the Dodger.

"A prime plant," observed Master Charley Bates.

Oliver looked from one to the other, with the greatest surprise; but he was not permitted to make any inquiries; for the two boys walked stealthily across the road, and slunk close behind the old gentleman towards whom his attention had been directed. Oliver walked a few paces after them;

and, not knowing whether to advance or retire, stood looking on in silent amazement.

The old gentleman was a very respectable-looking personage, with a powdered head and gold spectacles. He was dressed in a bottle-green coat with a black velvet collar; wore white trousers; and carried a smart bamboo cane under his arm. He had taken up a book from the stall, and there he stood, reading away, as hard as if he were in his elbow-chair, in his own study. It is very possible that he fancied himself there, indeed; for it was plain, from his utter abstraction, that he saw not the book-stall, nor the street, nor the boys, nor, in short, anything but the book itself; which he was reading straight through; turning over the leaf when he got to the bottom of a page, beginning at the top line of the next one, and going regularly on, with the greatest interest and eagerness.

What was Oliver's horror and alarm as he stood a few paces off, looking on with his eyelids as wide open as they would possibly go, to see the Dodger plunge his hand into the old gentleman's pocket and draw from thence a handkerchief! To see him hand the same to Charley Bates; and finally to behold them, both, running away around the corner at full speed!

In an instant the whole mystery of the handkerchiefs, and the watches, and the jewels, rushed upon the boy's mind. He stood, for a moment, with the blood so tingling through all his veins from terror, that he felt as if he were in a burning fire; then, confused and frightened, he took to his heels and, not knowing what he did, made off as fast as he could lay his feet to the ground.

This was all done in a minute's space. In the very instant when Oliver began to run, the old gentleman, putting his hand to his pocket, and missing his handkerchief, turned sharp round. Seeing the boy scudding away at such a rapid pace, he very naturally concluded him to be the depredator; and, shouting "Stop thief!" with all his might made off after him, book in hand.

But the old gentleman was not the only person who raised the hue-and-cry. The Dodger and Master Bates, unwilling to attract public attention by running down the open street, had merely retired into the very first doorway round the corner. They no sooner heard the cry, and saw Oliver running, than, guessing exactly how the matter stood, they issued forth with great promptitude and, shouting "Stop thief!" too, joined in the pursuit like good citizens.

Although Oliver had been brought up by philosophers, he was not theoretically acquainted with the beautiful axiom that self-preservation is the first law of nature. If he had been, perhaps he would have been prepared for this. Not being prepared, however, it alarmed him the more; so away he went like the wind, with the old gentleman and the two boys roaring and shouting behind him.

"Stop thief! Stop thief!" There is a magic in the sound. The tradesman leaves his counter, and the carman his wagon; the butcher throws down his tray; the baker his basket; the milkman his pail; the errand-boy his parcels; the schoolboy

OLIVER'S FIRST MEETING WITH THE ARTFUL DODGER

his marbles; the pavior his pickaxe; the child his battledore. Away they run, pell-mell, helter-skelter, slap-dash: tearing, yelling, and screaming: knocking down the passengers as they turn the corners, rousing up the dogs, and astonishing the fowls: and streets, squares, and courts re-echo with the sound.

"Stop thief! Stop thief!" The cry is taken up by a hundred voices, and the crowd accumulates at every turning. Away they fly, splashing through the mud, and rattling along the pavements: up go the windows, out run the people, onward bear the mob, a whole audience desert Punch in the very thickest of the plot, and, joining the rushing throng, swell the shout, and lend fresh vigor to the cry, "Stop thief! Stop thief!"

"Stop thief! Stop thief!" There is a passion *for hunting something* deeply implanted in the human breast. One wretched breathless child, panting with exhaustion; terror in his looks; agony in his eyes; large drops of perspiration streaming down his face; strains every nerve to make head upon his pursuers; and as they follow on his track, and gain upon him every instant, they hail his decreasing strength with still louder shouts, and whoop and scream with joy. "Stop thief!" Ay, stop him for God's sake, were it only in mercy!

Stopped at last. A clever blow. He is down upon the pavement; and the crowd eagerly gather round him: each newcomer, jostling and struggling with the others to catch a glimpse. "Stand aside!" "Give him a little air!" "Nonsense! he don't deserve it." "Where's the gentleman?"

"Here he is, coming down the street." "Make room there for the gentleman!" "Is this the boy, sir!" "Yes."

Oliver lay, covered with mud and dust, and bleeding from the mouth, looking wildly round upon the heap of faces that surrounded him, when the old gentleman was officiously dragged and pushed into the circle by the foremost of the pursuers.

"Yes," said the gentleman, "I am afraid it is."

"Afraid!" murmured the crowd. "That's a good 'un."

"Poor fellow!" said the gentleman, "he has hurt himself."

"*I* did that, sir," said a great lubberly fellow, stepping forward; "and preciously I cut my knuckle agin his mouth. *I* stopped him, sir."

The fellow touched his hat with a grin, expecting something for his pains; but the old gentleman, eyeing him with an expression of dislike, looked anxiously round, as if he contemplated running away himself: which it is very possible he might have attempted to do, and thus afforded another chase, had not a police officer (who is generally the last person to arrive in such cases) at that moment made his way through the crowd, and seized Oliver by the collar.

"Come, get up," said the man, roughly.

"It wasn't me indeed, sir. Indeed, indeed, it was two other boys," said Oliver, clasping his hands passionately, and looking round. "They are here somewhere."

"Oh no, they ain't," said the officer. He meant this to be ironical, but it was true besides; for the Dodger and Charley

Bates had filed off down the first convenient court they came to. "Come, get up!"

"Don't hurt him," said the old gentleman, compassionately.

"Oh no, I won't hurt him," replied the officer, tearing his jacket half off his back, in proof thereof. "Come, I know you; it won't do. Will you stand upon your legs, you young devil?"

Oliver, who could hardly stand, made a shift to raise himself on his feet, and was at once lugged along the streets by the jacket-collar, at a rapid pace. The gentleman walked on with them by the officer's side; and as many of the crowd as could achieve the feat, got a little ahead, and stared back at Oliver from time to time. The boys shouted in triumph; and on they went.

. . . .

Fortunately this time things turned out for the best for Oliver. The old gentleman, whose name was Brownlow, believed his story and took him to his own home, where he treated him as if he were his own son. They lived in a pleasant house on a quiet street, and Mrs. Brownlow was as kind as her husband.

This was only one of the adventures of Oliver Twist. He always seemed to be falling in with unusually bad people, and then being rescued by unusually kind people, who lost no time in receiving him as one of the family. The changes in his fortune were as sudden as those in the *Arabian Nights*. But then everything came out right in the end.

THE JELLYBY CHILDREN

IX

THE JELLYBY CHILDREN

TO know the Jellyby children you must know their mother. Mrs. Jellyby had a very kind heart and wanted to do good. Unfortunately the people she wanted to do good to lived a long way off. This was very inconvenient, as it was very difficult to get at them, especially as she didn't know their names or what they looked like. The people she was particularly interested in lived in Borrioboola-Gha, on the left bank of the Niger, in Africa. Mrs. Jellyby had to write a great many letters to all sorts of people about the state of things in Borrioboola-Gha, and this took up the time she might otherwise have given to her children.

What Mrs. Jellyby would have done if she had lived in Africa, we do not know. But in London she didn't find much to interest her: everything was too near. So the little Jellybys were left to grow up as best they could. There was no one whose business it was to see that they were properly fed or clothed or taught how to behave. Mrs. Jellyby couldn't look after them, because she was too busy making plans for the Africans. And Mr. Jellyby couldn't do it, for he had to listen to Mrs. Jellyby and do errands for her. So nobody did it, and the little Jellybys got on as best they could, which was not very well.

THE CHILDREN OF DICKENS

In *Bleak House,* Dickens makes Miss Summerson tell of
her visit to Mrs. Jellyby.

. . . . . .

We were to pass the night, Mr. Kenge told us, at Mrs.
Jellyby's; and then he turned to me, and said that he took it
for granted that I knew who Mrs. Jellyby was.

"I really don't, sir," I returned.

"In-deed! Mrs. Jellyby is a lady of great strength of
character. She devotes herself entirely to the public."

"And Mr. Jellyby, sir?"

"Ah! Mr. Jellyby," said Mr. Kenge, "I do not know
that I can describe Mr. Jellyby better than by saying he is
the husband of Mrs. Jellyby."

We arrived at our destination and found a crowd of people, mostly children, about the house at which we stopped,
which had a tarnished brass plate on the door, with the inscription, JELLYBY.

"Don't be frightened!" said Mr. Guppy, looking in at
the coach-window. "One of the young Jellybys been and
got his head through the area railings!"

"Oh, poor child," said I, "let me out, if you please!"

"Pray be careful of yourself, miss. The young Jellybys
are always up to something," said Mr. Guppy.

I made my way to the poor child, who was one of the dir-
tiest little unfortunates I ever saw, and found him very hot
and frightened, and crying loudly, fixed by the neck between
two iron railings, while a milkman and a beadle, with the
kindest intentions possible, were endeavoring to drag him

back by the legs, under a general impression that his skull was compressible by those means. As I found (after pacifying him) that he was a little boy, with a naturally large head, I thought that, perhaps, where his head could go, his body could follow, and mentioned that the best mode of extrication might be to push him forward. This was so favorably received by the milkman and beadle, that he would immediately have been pushed into the area, if I had not held his pinafore, while Richard and Mr. Guppy ran down through the kitchen, to catch him when he should be released. At last he was happily got down without any accident, and then he began to beat Mr. Guppy with a hoop-stick in quite a frantic manner.

Nobody had appeared belonging to the house, except a person in pattens, who had been poking at the child from below with a broom; I don't know with what object, and I don't think she did. I therefore supposed that Mrs. Jellyby was not at home; and was quite surprised when the person appeared in the passage without the pattens, and going up to the back room on the first floor, before Ada and me, announced us as, "Them two young ladies, Missis Jellyby!" We passed several more children on the way up, whom it was difficult to avoid treading on in the dark; and as we came into Mrs. Jellyby's presence, one of the poor little things fell down-stairs — down a whole flight (as it sounded to me), with a great noise.

Mrs. Jellyby, whose face reflected none of the uneasiness which we could not help showing in our own faces, as the dear

child's head recorded its passage with a bump on every stair
— Richard afterwards said he counted seven, besides one
for the landing — received us with perfect equanimity. She
was a pretty, very diminutive, plump woman, of from forty
to fifty, with handsome eyes, though they had a curious
habit of seeming to look a long way off. As if — I am quoting
Richard again — they could see nothing nearer than Africa!

"I am very glad indeed," said Mrs. Jellyby, in an agreeable voice, "to have the pleasure of receiving you. I have a
great respect for Mr. Jarndyce; and no one in whom he is interested can be an object of indifference to me."

We expressed our acknowledgments, and sat down behind
the door, where there was a lame invalid of a sofa. Mrs.
Jellyby had very good hair, but was too much occupied with
her African duties to brush it. The shawl in which she had
been loosely muffled, dropped on to her chair when she advanced to us; and as she turned to resume her seat, we could
not help noticing that her dress didn't nearly meet up the back,
and that the open space was railed across with a lattice-work
of stay-lace — like a summer-house.

The room, which was strewn with papers and nearly filled
by a great writing-table covered with similar litter, was, I
must say, not only very untidy, but very dirty. We were
obliged to take notice of that with our sense of sight, even
while, with our sense of hearing, we followed the poor child
who had tumbled down-stairs: I think into the back kitchen,
where somebody seemed to stifle him.

But what principally struck us was a jaded, and un-healthy-looking, though by no means plain girl, at the writing-table, who sat biting the feather of her pen, and staring at us. I suppose nobody ever was in such a state of ink. And, from her tumbled hair to her pretty feet, which were disfigured with frayed and broken satin slippers trodden down at heel, she really seemed to have no article of dress upon her, from a pin upwards, that was in its proper condition or its right place.

"You find me, my dears," said Mrs. Jellyby, snuffing the two great office candles in tin candlesticks which made the room taste strongly of hot tallow (the fire had gone out, and there was nothing in the grate but ashes, a bundle of wood, and a poker), "you find me, my dears, as usual, very busy; but that you will excuse. The African project at present employs my whole time. It involves me in correspondence with public bodies, and with private individuals anxious for the welfare of their species all over the country. I am happy to say it is advancing. We hope by this time next year to have from a hundred and fifty to two hundred healthy families cultivating coffee and educating the natives of Borrioboola-Gha, on the left bank of the Niger."

As Ada said nothing, but looked at me, I said it must be very gratifying.

"It *is* gratifying," said Mrs. Jellyby. "It involves the devotion of all my energies, such as they are; but that is nothing, so that it succeeds; and I am more confident of success every day. Do you know, Miss Summerson, I almost wonder that *you* never turned your thoughts to Africa."

This application of the subject was really so unexpected

[95]

to me, that I was quite at a loss how to receive it. I hinted that the climate ——

"The finest climate in the world!" said Mrs. Jellyby.

"Indeed, ma'am?"

"Certainly. With precaution," said Mrs. Jellyby. "You may go into Holborn, without precaution, and be run over. You may go into Holborn, with precaution, and never be run over. Just so with Africa."

I said, "No doubt" — I meant as to Holborn.

"If you would like," said Mrs. Jellyby, putting a number of papers towards us, "to look over some remarks on that head, and on the general subject (which have been extensively circulated), while I finish a letter I am now dictating — to my eldest daughter, who is my amanuensis ——"

The girl at the table left off biting her pen, and made a return to our recognition, which was half bashful and half sulky.

"I shall then have finished for the present," proceeded Mrs. Jellyby, with a sweet smile; "though my work is never done. Where are you, Caddy?"

"'— Presents her compliments to Mr. Swallow, and begs —'" said Caddy.

"'And begs,'" said Mrs. Jellyby, dictating, "'to inform him, in reference to his letter of inquiry on the African project —' No, Peepy! Not on any account!"

Peepy (so self-named) was the unfortunate child who had fallen down-stairs, who now interrupted the correspondence by presenting himself, with a strip of plaster on his forehead, to exhibit his wounded knees, in which Ada and I did not know which to pity most — the bruises or the dirt. Mrs. Jellyby merely added, "Go along, you naughty Peepy!" and fixed her fine eyes on Africa again.

However, as she at once proceeded with her dictation, and as I interrupted nothing by doing it, I ventured quietly to stop poor Peepy as he was going out, and to take him up to nurse. He looked very much astonished at it, and at Ada's kissing him; but soon fell fast asleep in my arms, sobbing at longer and longer intervals, until he was quiet. I was so occupied with Peepy that I lost the letter in detail, though I derived such a general impression from it of the momentous importance of Africa, and the utter insignificance of all other places and things, that I felt quite ashamed to have thought so little about it.

"Six o'clock!" said Mrs. Jellyby. "And our dinner hour nominally (for we dine at all hours) five! Caddy, show Miss Clare and Miss Summerson their rooms. You will like to make some change, perhaps? You will excuse me, I know, being so much occupied. Oh, that very bad child! Pray put him down, Miss Summerson!"

I begged permission to retain him, truly saying that he was not at all troublesome; and carried him up-stairs and laid him on my bed. Ada and I had two upper rooms, with a door of communication between. They were excessively bare and disorderly, and the curtain to my window was fastened up with a fork.

"You would like some hot water, wouldn't you?" said

Miss Jellyby, looking round for a jug with a handle to it, but looking in vain.

"If it is not being troublesome," said we.

"Oh, it's not the trouble," returned Miss Jellyby; "the question is, if there *is* any."

The evening was so very cold, and the rooms had such a marshy smell, that I must confess it was a little miserable; and Ada was half crying. We soon laughed, however, and were busily unpacking, when Miss Jellyby came back to say, that she was sorry there was no hot water; but they couldn't find the kettle, and the boiler was out of order.

We begged her not to mention it, and made all the haste we could to get down to the fire again. But all the little children had come up to the landing outside, to look at the phenomenon of Peepy lying on my bed; and our attention was distracted by the constant apparition of noses and fingers in situations of danger between the hinges of the doors. It was impossible to shut the door of either room; for my lock, with no knob to it, looked as if it wanted to be wound up; and though the handle of Ada's went round and round with the greatest smoothness, it was attended with no effect whatever on the door. Therefore I proposed to the children that they should come in and be very good at my table, and I would tell them the story of Little Red Riding Hood while I dressed; which they did, and were as quiet as mice, including Peepy, who awoke opportunely before the appearance of the wolf.

Soon after seven o'clock, we went down to dinner. The dinner was long, because of such accidents as the dish of potatoes being mislaid in the coal scuttle. Mrs. Jellyby paid no attention to such matters and told us all about the various committees, and the five thousand circulars that were sent out. After dinner, Mr. Jellyby sat in a corner in a state of great dejection. I sat in another and told Peepy, in whispers, the story of Puss in Boots, until Mrs. Jellyby, accidentally remembering the children, sent them to bed. As Peepy cried for me to take him, I carried him upstairs.

"What a strange house!" said Ada, when we got upstairs.

"My love," said I, "it quite confuses me. I can't understand it."

"What?" asked Ada.

"All this, my dear," said I. "It *must* be very good of Mrs. Jellyby to take such pains about a scheme for the benefit of Natives — and yet — Peepy and the housekeeping!"

SISSY JUPE

X

SISSY JUPE

DICKENS called the novel in which Sissy Jupe appears *Hard Times*. It was certainly hard times for children who had to go to the kind of schools that Mr. Thomas Gradgrind believed in. Mr. Gradgrind was a big square man, with a square coat and square shoulders, who thought that he knew all about education. He thought that the children in the schoolroom were like so many little pitchers, and the teacher's business was to fill them with facts.

"Now, what I want is Facts," said Mr. Gradgrind. "Teach these boys and girls nothing but Facts. This is the principle on which I bring up my own children, and this is the principle for these children. Stick to Facts."

Mr. Gradgrind, with another gentleman, had come to visit the school. Now Sissy Jupe was a bright little girl who would really enjoy using her own mind, but she didn't know how to use Mr. Gradgrind's mind, and she was very much upset when the great man pointed his square finger at her and said:

.   .   .   .

"Girl number twenty. I don't know that girl. Who is that girl?"

"Sissy Jupe, sir," explained number twenty, blushing, standing up, and courtesying.

"Sissy is not a name," said Mr. Gradgrind. "Don't call yourself Sissy. Call yourself Cecilia."

"It's father as calls me Sissy, sir," returned the girl in a trembling voice, and with another courtesy.

"Then he has no business to do it," said Mr. Gradgrind. "Tell him he mustn't. Cecilia Jupe. Let me see. What is your father?"

"He belongs to the horse-riding, if you please, sir."

Mr. Gradgrind frowned, and waved off the objectionable calling with his hand.

"We don't want to know anything about that, here. You mustn't tell us about that, here. Your father breaks horses, don't he?"

"If you please, sir, when they can get any to break, they do break horses in the ring, sir."

"You mustn't tell us about the ring, here. Very well, then. Describe your father as a horsebreaker. He doctors sick horses, I dare say?"

"Oh yes, sir."

"Very well, then. He is a veterinary surgeon, a farrier, and horsebreaker. Give me your definition of a horse."

(Sissy Jupe thrown into the greatest alarm by this demand.)

"Girl number twenty unable to define a horse!" said Mr. Gradgrind, for the general behoof of all the little pitchers. "Girl number twenty possessed of no facts, in reference to one of the commonest of animals! Some boy's definition of a horse. Bitzer, yours."

[104]

SISSY JUPE

The square finger, moving here and there, lighted suddenly on Bitzer, perhaps because he chanced to sit in the same ray of sunlight which, darting in at one of the bare windows of the intensely whitewashed room, irradiated Sissy. For the boys and girls sat on the face of the inclined plane in two compact bodies, divided up the centre by a narrow interval; and Sissy, being at the corner of a row on the sunny side, came in for the beginning of a sunbeam, of which Bitzer, being at corner of a row on the other side, a few rows in advance, caught the end. But, whereas the girl was so dark-eyed and dark-haired that she seemed to receive a deeper and more lustrous color from the sun, when it shone upon her, the boy was so light-eyed and light-haired that the self-same rays appeared to draw out of him what little color he ever possessed. His cold eyes would hardly have been eyes, but for the short ends of lashes which, by bringing them into immediate contrast with something paler than themselves, expressed their form. His short-cropped hair might have been a mere continuation of the sandy freckles on his forehead and face. His skin was so unwholesomely deficient in the natural tinge that he looked as though, if it were cut, he would bleed white.

"Bitzer," said Thomas Gradgrind. "Your definition of a horse."

"Quadruped. Graminivorous. Forty teeth, namely twenty-four grinders, four eye-teeth, and twelve incisors. Sheds coat in the spring; in marshy countries, sheds hoofs too. Hoofs hard, but requiring to be shod with iron. Age known by marks in mouth." Thus (and much more) Bitzer.

"Now girl number twenty," said Mr. Gradgrind. "You know what a horse is." . . .

The third gentleman now slipped forth, briskly smiling.

"That's a horse. Now, let me ask you girls and boys, Would you paper a room with representations of horses?"

After a pause, one half of the children cried in chorus, "Yes, sir!" Upon which the other half, seeing in the gentleman's face that Yes was wrong, cried out in chorus, "No, sir!" — as the custom is, in these examinations.

"Of course, No. Why wouldn't you?"

A pause. One corpulent slow boy, with a wheezy manner of breathing, ventured the answer, "Because he wouldn't paper a room at all, but would paint it."

"You *must* paper it," said the gentleman, rather warmly.

"You must paper it," said Thomas Gradgrind, "whether you like it or not. Don't tell *us* you wouldn't paper it. What do you mean, boy?"

"I'll explain to you, then," said the gentleman, after another and a dismal pause, "why you wouldn't paper a room with representations of horses. Do you ever see horses walking up and down the sides of rooms in reality — in fact? Do you?"

"Yes, sir!" from one half. "No, sir!" from the other.

"Of course no," said the gentleman, with an indignant look at the wrong half. "Why, then, you are not to see anywhere, what you don't see in fact; you are not to have anywhere, what you don't have in fact. What is called Taste, is only another name for Fact."

Thomas Gradgrind nodded his approbation.

SISSY JUPE

"This is a new principle, a discovery, a great discovery," said the gentleman.

"Now, I'll try you again. Suppose you were going to carpet a room. Would you use a carpet having a representation of flowers upon it?"

There being a general conviction by this time that "No, sir!" was always the right answer to this gentleman, the chorus of No was very strong. Only a few feeble stragglers said Yes; among them Sissy Jupe.

"Girl number twenty," said the gentleman, smiling in the calm strength of knowledge.

Sissy blushed, and stood up.

"So you would carpet your room — or your husband's room, if you were a grown woman, and had a husband — with representations of flowers, would you," said the gentleman. "Why would you?"

"If you please sir, I am very fond of flowers," returned the girl.

"And is that why you would put tables and chairs upon them, and have people walking over them with heavy boots?"

"It wouldn't hurt them, sir. They wouldn't crush and wither, if you please, sir. They would be the pictures of what was very pretty and pleasant, and I would fancy ——"

"Ay, ay, ay! But you mustn't fancy," cried the gentleman, quite elated by coming so happily to his point. "That's it! You are never to fancy."

"You are not, Cecilia Jupe," Thomas Gradgrind solemnly repeated, "to do anything of that kind."

THE CHILDREN OF DICKENS

"Fact, fact, fact!" said the gentleman. And "Fact, fact, fact!" repeated Thomas Gradgrind.

"You are to be in all things regulated and governed," said the gentleman, "by fact. We hope to have, before long, a board of fact, composed of commissioners of fact, who will force the people to be a people of fact, and of nothing but fact. You must discard the word Fancy altogether. You have nothing to do with it. You are not to have, in any object of use or ornament, what would be a contradiction in fact. You don't walk upon flowers in fact; you cannot be allowed to walk upon flowers in carpets. You don't find that foreign birds and butterflies come and perch upon your crockery; you cannot be permitted to paint foreign birds and butterflies upon your crockery. You never meet with quadrupeds going up and down walls; you must not have quadrupeds represented upon walls. You must use," said the gentleman, "for all these purposes, combinations and modifications (in primary colors) of mathematical figures which are susceptible of proof and demonstration. This is the new discovery. This is fact. This is taste."

The girl courtesied, and sat down. She was very young, and she looked as if she were frightened by the matter-of-fact prospect the world afforded.

THE CHILD OF THE MARSHALSEA

XI

THE CHILD OF THE MARSHALSEA

WHEN Dickens wrote *Little Dorrit,* he must often have thought of the times when as a boy he went to see his father in the debtors' prison. As a shy little boy he had to do all sorts of errands which took him over the prison and through the narrow streets that were near it.

Amy Dorrit, or little Dorrit, as she was called, was born in the great rambling prison called the Marshalsea. It was the only home she knew. Her father had got into debt and was sent to prison until the debt was paid. Of course he couldn't pay it so long as he was locked up and not given a chance to earn anything. So there he stayed year after year till he had become the oldest inhabitant, and rather enjoyed the honor. But it was hard on little Dorrit.

She had one good friend, the officer who was called the turnkey, because he had the keys of the prison and was the one who locked the prisoners in. When she began to walk and talk, he bought her a little armchair, and gave her toys. She became very fond of the turnkey, and was delighted when he dressed and undressed her dolls.

After a while, little Dorrit began to wonder what the world outside the prison walls was like. She saw the turnkey turn his great key in the door and thought, how wonderful it would be to go out through it!

She sat by the barred window, looking out. "Thinking of the fields?" the turnkey said, one day.

"Where are they?" she asked.

"Why, they are over there, my dear," said the turnkey with a flourish of the keys. "Just about there."

"Does anybody open them, or shut them? Are they locked?"

"Well," he said, "not in general."

"Are they pretty, Bob?" She called him Bob because he asked her to.

"Lovely. Full of flowers. There's buttercups and there's daisies, and there's — dandelions and all manner of games."

"Is it pleasant to be there, Bob?"

"Prime," said the turnkey.

"Was father ever there?"

"Oh, yes. He was there sometimes."

"Is he sorry not to be there now?"

"N — not particular," said the turnkey.

"Nor any of the people? Oh, are you quite sure and certain, Bob?"

Bob changed the subject, but this was the beginning of little Sunday excursions which these two curious companions took. Every other Sunday afternoon the turnkey would open the prison doors with his big key and would go off with little Dorrit into the green fields. He would pick out some meadow or green lane and light his pipe, while the little girl would gather grasses and wild flowers to bring home to her father.

THE CHILD OF THE MARSHALSEA

After some years had passed, Mr. Dorrit was released from prison and his fortune was restored, but little Dorrit always remembered the kind turnkey who had given her the first happy hours in the green fields.

THE CRATCHITS

XII

THE CRATCHITS

EVERYBODY knows the Cratchits. When Christmas comes people take up *A Christmas Carol* and turn to the account of the Christmas dinner which Bob Cratchit and his family enjoyed in their poor little house in the suburbs of London. Here it is just as Dickens wrote it.

.   .   .   .

Then up rose Mrs. Cratchit, Cratchit's wife, dressed out but poorly in a twice-turned gown, but brave in ribbons, which are cheap and make a goodly show for sixpence; and she laid the cloth, assisted by Belinda Cratchit, second of her daughters, also brave in ribbons; while Master Peter Cratchit plunged a fork into the saucepan of potatoes, and getting the corners of his monstrous shirt collar (Bob's private property, conferred upon his son and heir in honor of the day) into his mouth, rejoiced to find himself so gallantly attired, and yearned to show his linen in the fashionable parks. And now two smaller Cratchits, boy and girl, came tearing in, screaming that outside the baker's they had smelled the goose and known it for their own; and basking in luxurious thoughts of sage-and-onion, these young Cratchits danced about the table, and exalted Master Peter Cratchit to the skies, while he (not proud, although his collar nearly choked him) blew the fire, until

[117]

the slow potatoes bubbling up, knocked loudly at the saucepan-lid to be let out and peeled.

"What has ever got your precious father then?" said Mrs. Cratchit. "And your brother, Tiny Tim! And Martha warn't as late last Christmas Day by half-an-hour!"

"Here's Martha, mother!" said a girl, appearing as she spoke.

"Here's Martha, mother!" cried the two young Cratchits. "Hurrah! There's *such* a goose, Martha!"

"Why, bless your heart alive, my dear, how late you are!" said Mrs. Cratchit, kissing her a dozen times, and taking off her shawl and bonnet for her with officious zeal.

"We'd a deal of work to finish up last night," replied the girl, "and had to clear away this morning, mother!"

"Well! Never mind so long as you are come," said Mrs. Cratchit. "Sit ye down before the fire, my dear, and have a warm, Lord bless ye!"

"No, no! There's father coming," cried the two young Cratchits, who were everywhere at once. "Hide, Martha, hide!"

So Martha hid herself, and in came little Bob, the father, with at least three feet of comforter exclusive of the fringe, hanging down before him; and his threadbare clothes darned up and brushed, to look seasonable; and Tiny Tim upon his shoulder. Alas for Tiny Tim, he bore a little crutch, and had his limbs supported by an iron frame!

"Why, where's our Martha?" cried Bob Cratchit, looking round.

TINY TIM AND BOB CRATCHIT ON CHRISTMAS DAY

"Not coming," said Mrs. Cratchit.

"Not coming!" said Bob, with a sudden declension in his high spirits; for he had been Tim's blood horse all the way from church, and had come home rampant. "Not coming upon Christmas Day!"

Martha didn't like to see him disappointed, if it were only in joke; so she came out prematurely from behind the closet door, and ran into his arms, while the two young Cratchits hustled Tiny Tim, and bore him off into the wash-house, that he might hear the pudding singing in the copper.

"And how did little Tim behave?" asked Mrs. Cratchit, when she had rallied Bob on his credulity, and Bob had hugged his daughter to his heart's content.

"As good as gold," said Bob, "and better. Somehow he gets thoughtful, sitting by himself so much, and thinks the strangest things you ever heard. He told me, coming home, that he hoped the people saw him in the church, because he was a cripple, and it might be pleasant to them to remember upon Christmas Day, who made lame beggars walk and blind men see."

Bob's voice was tremulous when he told them this, and trembled more when he said that Tiny Tim was growing strong and hearty.

His active little crutch was heard upon the floor, and back came Tiny Tim before another word was spoken, escorted by his brother and sister to his stool before the fire; and while Bob, turning up his cuffs — as if, poor fellow, they were capable of being made more shabby — compounded some hot mixture in a jug with gin and lemons, and stirred it round and round and put it on the hob to simmer, Master Peter, and the two ubiquitous young Cratchits went to fetch the goose, with which they soon returned in high procession.

Such a bustle ensued that you might have thought a goose the rarest of all birds; a feathered phenomenon, to which a black swan was a matter of course — and in truth it was something very like it in that house. Mrs. Cratchit made the gravy (ready beforehand in a little saucepan) hissing hot; Master Peter mashed the potatoes with incredible vigor; Miss Belinda sweetened up the apple sauce; Martha dusted the hot plates; Bob took Tiny Tim beside him in a tiny corner at the table; the two young Cratchits set chairs for everybody, not forgetting themselves, and mounting guard upon their posts, crammed spoons into their mouths, lest they should shriek for goose before their turn came to be helped. At last the dishes were set on, and grace was said. It was succeeded by a breathless pause, as Mrs. Cratchit, looking slowly all along the carving-knife, prepared to plunge it in the breast; but when she did, and when the long expected gush of stuffing issued forth, one murmur of delight arose all round the board, and even Tiny Tim, excited by the two young Cratchits, beat on the table with the handle of his knife, and feebly cried Hurrah!

There never was such a goose. Bob said he didn't believe there ever was such a goose cooked. Its tenderness and flavor, size and cheapness, were the themes of universal admiration. Eked out by the apple sauce and mashed potatoes, it was a

THE CRATCHITS

sufficient dinner for the whole family; indeed, as Mrs. Cratchit said with great delight (surveying one small atom of a bone upon the dish) they hadn't ate it all at last! Yet every one had had enough, and the youngest Cratchits, in particular, were steeped in sage and onion to the eyebrows! But now, the plates being changed by Miss Belinda, Mrs. Cratchit left the room alone — too nervous to bear witnesses — to take the pudding up and bring it in.

Suppose it should not be done enough! Suppose it should break in turning out! Suppose somebody should have got over the wall of the back-yard, and stolen it while they were merry with the goose — a supposition at which the two young Cratchits became livid! All sorts of horrors were supposed.

Hallo! A great deal of steam! The pudding was out of the copper. A smell like a washing-day! That was the cloth. A smell like an eating-house and a pastrycook's next door to each other, with a laundress's next door to that! That was the pudding! In half a minute Mrs. Cratchit entered — flushed, but smiling proudly — with the pudding like a speckled cannon-ball so hard and firm blazing in half of half-a-quartern of ignited brandy, and bedight with Christmas holly stuck into the top.

Oh, a wonderful pudding! Bob Cratchit said, and calmly too, that he regarded it as the greatest success achieved by Mrs. Cratchit since their marriage. Mrs. Cratchit said that now the weight was off her mind, she would confess she had had her doubts about the quantity of flour. Everybody had something to say about it, but nobody said or thought it was at all a small pudding for a large family. It would have been flat heresy to do so. Any Cratchit would have blushed to hint at such a thing.

At last the dinner was all done, the cloth was cleared, the hearth swept, and the fire made up. The compound in the jug being tasted, and considered perfect, apples and oranges were put upon the table, and a shovelful of chestnuts on the fire. Then all the Cratchit family drew round the hearth, in what Bob Cratchit called a circle, meaning half a one; and at Bob Cratchit's elbow stood the family display of glass. Two tumblers, and a custard-cup without a handle.

These held the hot stuff from the jug, however, as well as golden goblets would have done; and Bob served it out with beaming looks, while the chestnuts on the fire sputtered and cracked noisily. Then Bob proposed:

"A Merry Christmas to us all, my dears. God bless us!"

Which all the family re-echoed.

"God bless us every one!" said Tiny Tim, the last of all.

THE DOLL'S DRESSMAKER

XIII

THE DOLL'S DRESSMAKER

THE fact that Dickens when he was only twelve years old was put to work and had to make his own living made him feel old when he was really very young. He had to look after himself as if he had been a man. In *Our Mutual Friend* he gives us a picture of an old young person, Jenny Wren, the Doll's Dressmaker, who talked as if she were forty, when she was only twelve and small for her age. Her father was a drunkard and she had been compelled to act as head of the house.

She was a queer little person with bright, snapping eyes and a sharp tongue. She sat in a little old-fashioned armchair which had a little working-bench before it. She had set up in business as a doll's dressmaker and manufacturer of pin-cushions and pen-wipers.

If you were in London you would have to go a long way to find the Doll's Dressmaker. First you crossed Westminster Bridge, and then you came to a certain little street called Church Street, and then to an out-of-the-way square called Smith Square, in the centre of which was a very ugly church. Then you came to a blacksmith-shop and a lumber-yard, and a dealer in old iron. There was a rusty portion of an old boiler that you had to walk around. Beyond that there were several little quiet houses in a row. In one of these houses was the little Doll's Dressmaker. That was the way Bradley Headstone and Charley Hexam found the house where Jenny Wren lived.

They knocked at the door and saw a queer little figure sitting in an armchair.

"I can't get up," said the child, "because my back's bad and my legs are queer. But I'm the person of the house. What do you want, young man?"

"I wanted to see my sister."

"Many young men have sisters. Give me your name, young man."

"Hexam is my name.

"Ah, indeed?" said the person of the house. "I thought it might be. Your sister will be in, in about a quarter of an hour. I am very fond of your sister. She's my particular friend. Take a seat. And this gentleman's name?"

"Mr. Headstone, my schoolmaster."

"Take a seat. And would you please to shut the street door first? I can't very well do it myself, because my back's so bad, and my legs are so queer."

They complied in silence, and the little figure went on with its work of gumming and gluing together with a camel's-hair brush certain pieces of cardboard and thin wood, previously cut into various shapes. The scissors and knives upon the bench showed that the child herself had cut them; and the bright scraps of velvet and silk and ribbon also strewn upon the bench showed that when duly stuffed (and stuffing too was there) she was to cover them smartly. The dexterity of her nimble fingers was remarkable, and, as she brought two

JENNY WREN, THE LITTLE DOLLS' DRESSMAKER

thin edges accurately together by giving them a little bite, she would glance at the visitors out of the corners of her gray eyes with a look that outsharpened all her other sharpness.

"You can't tell me the name of my trade, I'll be bound," she said, after taking several of these observations.

"You make pincushions," said Charley.

"What else do I make?"

"Pen-wipers," said Bradley Headstone.

"Ha! ha! What else do I make? You're a schoolmaster, but you can't tell me."

"You do something," he returned, pointing to a corner of the little bench, "with straw; but I don't know what."

"Well done you!" cried the person of the house. "I only make pincushions and pen-wipers to use up my waste. But my straw really does belong to my business. Try again. What do I make with my straw?"

"Dinner-mats."

"A schoolmaster, and says dinner-mats! I'll give you a clue to my trade, in a game of forfeits. I love my love with a B because she's Beautiful; I hate my love with a B because she is Brazen; I took her to the sign of the Blue Boar, and I treated her with Bonnets; her name's Bouncer, and she lives in Bedlam. — Now, what do I make with my straw?"

"Ladies' bonnets?"

"Fine ladies'," said the person of the house, nodding assent. "Dolls'. I'm a Doll's Dressmaker."

"I hope it's a good business?"

The person of the house shrugged her shoulders and shook

her head. "No. Poorly paid. And I'm often so pressed for time!" I had a doll married, last week, and was obliged to work all night. And it's not good for me, on account of my back being so bad and my legs so queer."

They looked at the little creature with a wonder that did not diminish, and the schoolmaster said: "I am sorry your fine ladies are so inconsiderate."

"It's the way with them," said the person of the house, shrugging her shoulders again. "And they take no care of their clothes, and they never keep to the same fashions a month. I work for a doll with three daughters. Bless you, she's enough to ruin her husband!"

The person of the house gave a weird little laugh here, and gave them another look out of the corners of her eyes. She had an elfin chin that was capable of great expression; and whenever she gave this look, she hitched this chin up. As if her eyes and her chin worked together on the same wires.

"Are you always as busy as you are now?"

"Busier. I'm slack just now. I finished a large mourning order the day before yesterday. Doll I work for lost a canary-bird." The person of the house gave another little laugh, and then nodded her head several times, as who should moralize, "Oh this world, this world!"

"Are you alone all day?" asked Bradley Headstone. "Don't any of the neighboring children —— ?"

"Ah, lud!" cried the person of the house, with a little scream, as if the word had pricked her. "Don't talk of children. I can't bear children. *I* know their tricks and their manners."

She said this with an angry little shake of her right fist close before her eyes.

Perhaps it scarcely required the teacher-habit to perceive that the doll's dressmaker was inclined to be bitter on the difference between herself and other children. But both master and pupil understood it so.

"Always running about and screeching, always playing and fighting, always skip-skip-skipping on the pavement and chalking it for their games! Oh! *I* know their tricks and their manners!" Shaking the little fist as before. "And that's not all. Ever so often calling names in through a person's keyhole, and imitating a person's back and legs. Oh! *I* know their tricks and their manners. And I'll tell you what I'd do to punish 'em. There's doors under the church in the Square — black doors, leading into black vaults. Well! I'd open one of those doors, and I'd cram 'em all in, and then I'd lock the door and through the keyhole I'd blow in pepper."

"What would be the good of blowing in pepper?" asked Charley Hexam.

"To set 'em sneezing," said the person of the house, "and make their eyes water. And when they were all sneezing and inflamed, I'd mock 'em through the keyhole. Just as they, with their tricks and their manners, mock a person through a person's keyhole!"

An uncommonly emphatic shake of her little fist close before her eyes seemed to ease the mind of the person of the house; for she added with recovered composure, "No, no, no. No children for me. Give me grown-ups."

LITTLE NELL

LITTLE NELL AND HER GRANDFATHER AT MRS. JARLEY'S

XIV

LITTLE NELL

ONE of the strange things about London is the number of little shops in out-of-the-way places, where they sell things that one would suppose nobody would be looking for. The shops seem hidden away, and the game is for the customers to find them. And very often the customers don't find them.

In one of these little streets was an old curiosity shop, kept by a little old man with long gray hair. The shop was full of old and curious things which the old man had collected and heaped upon the floor. There were suits of armor, and bits of old china and figures carved out of wood. The room was dark, and it was hard to walk around without stepping upon some of the curiosities.

The one bright spot in the old man's life was his love for his granddaughter, little Nell Trent. For her he had been saving everything he could, but of late he had been losing more than he had gained. It would have been a rather dull life for little Nell if it had not been for Kit Nubbles.

Kit was a shock-headed, awkward boy who lived with his mother not far away, and he came every day to help Nell's grandfather in the shop. He had an uncommonly big mouth, very red cheeks, and an old hat without any brim. Kit liked to "show off," especially when Nell was around. He had a remarkable way of standing sideways as he spoke and thrusting his head over his shoulders. When he found that it would make Nell laugh, he did it again and again.

And there was a dwarf named Quilp who was as ugly as he looked, and delighted in nothing so much as in making everybody afraid of him. He lived down by the river. He had a business of his own. He bought old copper and rusty anchors from ships that had been broken up. But his real occupation was in making everybody who came under him miserable. At last Nell and her grandfather, in order to escape from Quilp, made up their minds to leave London, and go off into the country where they might find peace. They didn't care where they went so that Quilp could not follow them. This would have been a very good plan if they had had money for their journeys, but as they hadn't they had to depend on the kindness of the people on the road.

In their wanderings Nell and her grandfather fell in with some queer people. While they were resting near a village church, they came upon two men who were travelling over the country giving Punch and Judy shows. One of them, a merry-faced man with twinkling eyes and a red nose, was named Short. His companion, Codlin, was a more courteous and gloomy person. Mr. Codlin took the figure of Judy out of the box and said:

"Look here, here's all this Judy's clothes falling to pieces again. You haven't got a needle and thread, I suppose?"

Nell had a needle and thread and soon was at work on

Judy's dress, and soon they were friends, and Codlin and Short took them to the wayside inn where they met other travellers who were going to fairs. The chapter which tells of the talk at the Jolly Sandboys is one which the lover of Dickens likes to read more than once.

THE JOLLY SANDBOYS

THE Jolly Sandboys was a small roadside inn with a sign representing three Sandboys increasing their jollity with as many jugs of ale and bags of gold, creaking and swinging on its post on the opposite side of the road. As the travellers had observed that day, there were many indications of their drawing nearer and nearer to the race town, such as gypsy camps, carts laden with gambling booths, itinerant showmen of all kinds, and beggars and trampers of every degree.

Mr. Codlin entered the inn, where a mighty fire was blazing on the hearth and roaring up the wide chimney with a cheerful sound. There was a large iron kettle bubbling and simmering in the heat. And when the landlord lifted the lid, there was a savory smell. The glow of the fire was upon the landlord's bald head and upon his twinkling eyes. Mr. Codlin drew his sleeve across his lips and said in a murmuring voice, "What is it?"

"It's a stew of tripe," said the landlord, "and cowheel, and bacon," smacking his lips, "and steak, and peas, cauliflowers, new potatoes, and sparrow-grass, all working together in one delicious gravy."

Very soon all the hungry wayfarers were sitting down to supper while the rain fell in torrents on the roof.

. . . .

Supper was not yet over, when there arrived at the Jolly Sandboys two more travellers bound for the same haven as the rest, who had been walking in the rain for some hours, and came in shining and heavy with water. One of these was the proprieter of a giant, and a little lady without legs or arms, who had jogged forward in a van; the other, a silent gentleman who earned his living by showing tricks upon the cards, and who had rather deranged the natural expression of his countenance by putting small leaden lozenges into his eyes and bringing them out at his mouth, which was one of his professional accomplishments. The name of the first of these newcomers was Vuffin; the other, probably as a pleasant satire upon his ugliness, was called Sweet William. To render them as comfortable as he could, the landlord bestirred himself nimbly, and in a very short time both gentlemen were perfectly at their ease.

"How's the Giant?" said Short, when they all sat smoking round the fire.

"Rather weak upon his legs," returned Mr. Vuffin. "I begin to be afraid he's going at the knees."

"That's a bad lookout," said Short.

"Ay! Bad indeed," replied Mr. Vuffin, contemplating the fire with a sigh. "Once get a giant shaky on his legs, and the public care no more about him than they do for a dead cabbage-stalk."

[136]

LITTLE NELL

"What becomes of the old giants?" said Short, turning to him again after a little reflection.

"They're usually kept in caravans to wait upon the dwarfs," said Mr. Vuffin.

"The maintaining of 'em must come expensive, when they can't be shown, eh?" remarked Short, eyeing him doubtfully.

"It's better that, than letting 'em go upon the parish or about the streets," said Mr. Vuffin. "Once make a giant common and giants will never draw again. Look at wooden legs. If there was only one man with a wooden leg what a property *he'd* be!"

"So he would!" observed the landlord and Short both together. "That's very true."

"Instead of which," pursued Mr. Vuffin, "if you was to advertise Shakspeare played entirely by wooden legs, it's my belief you wouldn't draw a sixpence."

"I don't suppose you would," said Short. And the landlord said so too.

"This shows, you see," said Mr. Vuffin, waving his pipe with an argumentative air, "this shows the policy of keeping the used-up giants still in the carawans, where they get food and lodging for nothing, all their lives, and in general very glad they are to stop there. There was one giant — a black 'un — as left his carawan some years ago and took to carrying coach-bills about London, making himself as cheap as crossing-sweepers. He died. I make no insinuation against anybody in particular," said Mr. Vuffin, looking solemnly round, "but he was ruining the trade; — and he died."

The landlord drew his breath hard, and looked at the owner of the dogs, who nodded and said gruffly that *he* remembered.

"I know you do, Jerry," said Mr. Vuffin with profound meaning. "I know you remember it, Jerry, and the universal opinion was, that it served him right. Why, I remember the time when old Maunders as had three-and-twenty wans — I remember the time when old Maunders had in his cottage in Spa fields in the winter time when the season was over, eight male and female dwarfs setting down to dinner every day, who was waited on by eight old giants in green coats, red smalls, blue cotton stockings, and high-lows: and there was one dwarf as had grown elderly and wicious who whenever his giant wasn't quick enough to please him, used to stick pins in his legs, not being able to reach up any higher. I know that's a fact, for Maunders told it me himself."

"What about the dwarfs, when *they* get old?" inquired the landlord.

"The older a dwarf is, the better worth he is," returned Mr. Vuffin; "a gray-headed dwarf, well wrinkled, is beyond all suspicion. But a giant weak in the legs and not standing upright — keep him in the carawan, but never show him, never show him, for any persuasion that can be offered."

While Mr. Vuffin and his two friends smoked their pipes and beguiled the time with such conversation as this, the silent gentleman sat in a warm corner, swallowing, or seeming to swallow, a sixpennyworth of halfpence for practice, balancing a feather upon his nose, and rehearsing other feats

of dexterity of that kind, without paying any regard whatever to the company, who in their turn left him utterly un-
noticed. At length the weary child prevailed upon her grandfather to retire, and they withdrew, leaving the company
yet seated round the fire, and the dogs fast asleep at a hum-
ble distance.

MRS. JARLEY AND HER WAX–WORKS

OF all the adventures of little Nell, the meeting with
Mrs. Jarley was the most delightful. It happened
just at the right time. Nell and her grandfather
were trudging along the road. It was late in the afternoon
and they didn't know where they were to find a resting-place.
They came to a common and saw what in England is called
a caravan. It is not such a caravan as one would find in
Bagdad, made up of camels. It was a little house on wheels.
It had white curtains on the windows, and the window-
shutters were of green, with bright red trimmings. There
was a door with brass knockers and there were two fat horses
to draw it. They all belonged to a stout, good-natured lady
named Mrs. Jarley, who was at the moment arranging her
tea things for a comfortable afternoon tea.

Mrs. Jarley looked up and saw little Nell. "Are you
hungry, child?"

"Not very, but we are tired, and it's a long way."

"Well, hungry or not," said Mrs. Jarley, "you had better
have some tea, and I suppose the old gentleman is agreeable
to that."

So they sat down on the grass and had tea and bread and butter and generous slices of ham.

Then Mrs. Jarley invited Nell and her grandfather to be her guests in the little house on wheels. There wasn't very much room, but Mrs. Jarley was so hospitable that they at once accepted her invitation and made themselves at home. Half of the little house had berths for sleeping, very much as if it were a ship. The other half was a kitchen, with a little stove in it. It also had several boxes and kettles and saucepans.

When they got started after breakfast in the morning, little Nell's spirits rose and she forgot her troubles.

"Well," said Mrs. Jarley, "how do you like this way of travelling?"

Nell said she liked it very much.

"That's the happiness of you young people," said Mrs. Jarley. "You don't know what it is to be low in your feelings. You always have your appetites too — and what a comfort it is."

Then Mrs. Jarley brought out a large roll of canvas about a yard wide, and spread it on the floor.

"There, child," she said, "read that."

Nell walked down it, and read aloud, in enormous black letters, the inscription, "JARLEY'S WAX–WORK."

"Read it again," said the lady, complacently.

"Jarley's Wax-Work," repeated Nell.

"That's me," said the lady. "I am Mrs. Jarley."

Giving the child an encouraging look, intended to re-

assure her and let her know that, although she stood in the
presence of the original Jarley, she must not allow herself
to be utterly overwhelmed and borne down, the lady of the
caravan unfolded another scroll, whereon was the inscription, "One hundred figures the full size of life," and then
another scroll, on which was written, "The only stupendous
collection of real wax-work in the world," and then several
smaller scrolls with such inscriptions as, "Now exhibiting
within" — "The genuine and only Jarley" — "Jarley's un-
rivalled collection" — "Jarley is the delight of the Nobility
and Gentry" — "The Royal Family are the patrons of Jarley." When she had exhibited these leviathans of public
announcement to the astonished child, she brought forth
specimens of the lesser fry in the shape of handbills, some
of which were couched in the form of parodies on popular
melodies; as, "Believe me if all Jarley's wax-work so rare"
— "I saw thy show in youthful prime" — "Over the water
to Jarley"; while, to consult all tastes, others were composed
with a view to the lighter and more facetious spirits, as a
parody on the favorite air of "If I had a donkey," beginning:

> If I know'd a donkey wot wouldn't go
> To see Mrs. JARLEY's wax-work show,
> Do you think I'd acknowledge him?
> Oh no no!
> Then run to Jarley's ——

— besides several compositions in prose, purporting to be
dialogues between the Emperor of China and an oyster, or
the Archbishop of Canterbury and a Dissenter on the sub-

ject of church-rates, but all having the same moral, namely, that the reader must make haste to Jarley's, and that children and servants were admitted at half-price. When she had brought all these testimonials of her important position in society to bear upon her young companion, Mrs. Jarley rolled them up and, having put them carefully away, sat down again, and looked at the child in triumph.

"Never go into the company of a filthy Punch any more," said Mrs. Jarley, "after this."

"I never saw any wax-work, ma'am," said Nell. "Is it funnier than Punch?"

"Funnier!" said Mrs. Jarley in a shrill voice. "It is not funny at all."

"Oh!" said Nell, with all possible humility.

"It isn't funny at all," repeated Mrs. Jarley. "It's calm and — what's that word again — critical? — no — classical, that's it — it's calm and classical. No low beatings and knockings about, no jokings and squeakings like your precious Punches, but always the same, with a constantly unchanging air of coldness and gentility; and so like life, that if wax-work only spoke and walked about, you'd hardly know the difference. I won't go so far as to say, that, as it is, I've seen wax-work quite like life, but I've certainly seen some life that was exactly like wax-work."

"Is it here, ma'am?" asked Nell, whose curiosity was awakened by this description.

"Is what here, child?"

"The wax-work, ma'am."

"Why, bless you, child, what are you thinking of? How could such a collection be here, where you see everything except the inside of one little cupboard and a few boxes? It's gone on in the other wans to the assembly-rooms, and there it'll be exhibited the day after to-morrow. You are going to the same town, and you'll see it, I dare say. It's natural to expect that you'll see it, and I've no doubt you will. I suppose you couldn't stop away if you was to try ever so much."

"I shall not be in the town, I think, ma'am," said the child.

"Not there!" cried Mrs. Jarley. "Then where will you be?"

"I — I — don't quite know. I am not certain."

"You don't mean to say that you're travelling about the country without knowing where you're going to?" said the lady of the caravan. "What curious people you are! What line are you in? You looked to me at the races, child, as if you were quite out of your element, and had got there by accident."

"We were there quite by accident," returned Nell, confused by this abrupt questioning. "We are poor people, ma'am, and are only wandering about. We have nothing to do; — I wish we had."

"You amaze me more and more," said Mrs. Jarley, after remaining for some time as mute as one of her own figures. "Why, what do you call yourselves? Not beggars?"

"Indeed, ma'am, I don't know what else we are," returned the child.

[143]

"Lord bless me," said the lady of the caravan. "I never heard of such a thing. Who'd have thought it!"

She remained so long silent after this exclamation, that Nell feared she felt her having been induced to bestow her protection and conversation upon one so poor, to be an outrage upon her dignity that nothing could repair. This persuasion was rather confirmed than otherwise by the tone in which she at length broke silence, and said:

"And yet you can read. And write too, I shouldn't wonder?"

"Yes, ma'am," said the child, fearful of giving new offense by the confession.

"Well, and what a thing that is," returned Mrs. Jarley. "*I* can't."

Mrs. Jarley's wax-works were carried in other wagons to the town where they were to be exhibited, and little Nell was engaged to point to each wax figure, and explain to the audience what it represented. Dozens of figures of noted persons, all with wax faces, and all dressed in brilliant clothes, stood stiffly in a row.

Dickens describes the scene where Mrs. Jarley instructs Nell as to her duties:

.   .   .   .

When the festoons were all put up as tastily as they might be, the stupendous collection was uncovered, and there were displayed, on a raised platform some two feet from the floor, running round the room and parted from the rude public by a crimson rope breast high, divers sprightly effigies of celebrated characters, singly and in groups, clad in glittering dresses of various climes and times, and standing more or less unsteadily upon their legs, with their eyes very wide open, and their nostrils very much inflated, and the muscles of their legs and arms very strongly developed, and all their countenances expressing great surprise. All the gentlemen were very pigeon-breasted and very blue about the beards; and all the ladies were miraculous figures; and all the ladies and all the gentlemen were looking intensely nowhere, and staring with extraordinary earnestness at nothing.

When Nell had exhausted her first raptures at this glorious sight, Mrs. Jarley ordered the room to be cleared of all but herself and the child, and, sitting herself down in an armchair in the centre, formally invested her with a willow wand, long used by herself for pointing out the characters, and was at great pains to instruct her in her duty.

"That," said Mrs. Jarley in her exhibition tone, as Nell touched a figure at the beginning of the platform, "is an unfortunate Maid of Honor in the Time of Queen Elizabeth, who died from pricking her finger in consequence of working upon a Sunday. Observe the blood which is trickling from her finger; also the gold-eyed needle of the period, with which she is at work."

All this Nell repeated twice or thrice, pointing to the finger and the needle at the right times, and then passed on to the next.

"That, ladies and gentlemen," said Mrs. Jarley, "is Jasper Packlemerton of atrocious memory, who courted and married fourteen wives, and destroyed them all by tickling the soles of their feet when they were sleeping in the consciousness of innocence and virtue. On being brought to the scaffold and asked if he was sorry for what he had done, he replied yes, he was sorry for having let 'em off so easy, and hoped all Christian husbands would pardon him the offense. Let this be a warning to all young ladies to be particular in the character of the gentlemen of their choice. Observe that his fingers are curled as if in the act of tickling, and that his face is represented with a wink, as he appeared when committing his barbarous murders."

When Nell knew all about Mr. Packlemerton, and could say it without faltering, Mrs. Jarley passed on to the fat man, and then to the thin man, the tall man, the short man, the old lady who died of dancing at a hundred and thirty-two, the wild boy of the woods, the woman who poisoned fourteen families with pickled walnuts, and other historical characters and interesting but misguided individuals. And so well did Nell profit by her instructions, and so apt was she to remember them, that by the time they had been shut up together for a couple of hours, she was in full possession of the history of the whole establishment, and perfectly competent to the enlightenment of visitors.

Mrs. Jarley was not slow to express her admiration at this happy result, and carried her young friend and pupil to inspect the remaining arrangements within doors, by virtue of which the passage had been already converted into a grove of green baize hung with the inscriptions she had al-

ready seen (Mr. Slum's productions), and a highly ornamented table placed at the upper end for Mrs. Jarley herself,
at which she was to preside and take the money, in company
with his Majesty King George the Third, Mr. Grimaldi as
clown, Mary Queen of Scots, an anonymous gentleman of
the Quaker persuasion, and Mr. Pitt holding in his hand a
correct model of the bill for the imposition of the window
duty. The preparations without doors had not been neglected
either; for a nun of great personal attractions was telling her
beads on the little portico over the door; and a brigand with
the blackest possible head of hair, and the clearest possible
complexion, was at that moment going round the town in a
cart, consulting the miniature of a lady.

It now only remained that the compositions in praise of
the wax-works should be judiciously distributed; that the
pathetic effusions should find their way to all private houses
and tradespeople; and that the parody commencing "If I
know'd a donkey," should be confined to the taverns, and
circulated only among the lawyers' clerks and choice spirits
of the place. When this had been done, and Mrs. Jarley had
waited upon the boarding-schools in person, with a hand-
bill composed expressly for them, in which it was distinctly
proved that wax-work refined the mind, cultivated the taste,
and enlarged the sphere of the human understanding, that
lady sat down to dinner.

THE KENWIGSES

XV

THE KENWIGSES

I HAVE always wondered whether I should have liked the Kenwigses if I had met them in New York or Minneapolis. Probably I should not. But I like to read about them, and they somehow seem to be amusing and likeable. That is because they made a part of London once upon a time. They lived in a tumble-down house, in a tumble-down street. All the houses had seen better days and seemed to be nodding at each other as much as to say: "Times are not what they used to be when we were young."

But for all their dreary surroundings, the Kenwigses, big and little, were very cheery people, and had a remarkably good time. The great thing about them was that they admired each other so much, and told each other so. That doesn't seem to be very much. Anybody could do that, but most people don't. I have known very nice people to live together for years without ever telling one another how nice they are. In that way the niceness often disappears. It wasn't so with the Kenwigses. They made the most of each other and got a great deal of satisfaction out of a very little. They were all proud of the family, and didn't care who knew it.

They lived on the first floor of the house, which was never kept in a tidy condition. Mrs. Kenwigs put all her time in

keeping the little girls tidy, and I am not sure that any one
can blame her for the fact that the entry was always in disorder. Mr. Kenwigs was very proud of his wife, and Mrs.
Kenwigs was proud of her uncle, Mr. Lillyvick, whose business it was to collect water-rents in that neighborhood. He
would go about with his bills and knock loudly at the doors
of all the people who hadn't paid their water-rates, and
threaten them in a most terrifying manner. So every one
was afraid of Mr. Lillyvick except Mrs. Kenwigs, who was
proud of him. For she was his niece.

We are introduced to the Kenwigs children at a party,
which Mrs. Kenwigs made in order to show off her uncle to
the admiring neighbors. The reason why the children sat up
for the party was because it was held in the sitting-room,
which was also the place where they slept. It was a very
great occasion, and the children were on their good behavior.
Uncle Lillyvick was seated in a large armchair by the fire-
side, and the four little Kenwigses sat side by side on a
small bench facing the fire, with their nice little pig-tails tied
up with blue ribbons.

"They are so beautiful," said Mrs. Kenwigs, sobbing. It
was very easy for Mrs. Kenwigs to sob.

"Oh dear," said all the ladies, "but don't give way,
don't!"

"I can't help it," sobbed Mrs. Kenwigs. "Oh, they are
too beautiful to live, much too beautiful!"

On hearing this all the four little girls began to cry, too,
and hid their heads in their mother's lap. This made a great

MRS. KENWIGS AND THE FOUR LITTLE KENWIGSES

excitement. At last the little Kenwigses were distributed among the company, so that their mother might not be overcome by the sight of their combined beauty. Then the conversation was taken up again by the older people. When it threatened to stop, Mrs. Kenwigs turned to Morleena, the oldest of the little girls.

"Morleena Kenwigs, kiss your dear uncle." Morleena obeyed, and then the three other little girls had to do the same thing, and then they had to kiss all the other members of the company. Then Morleena, who had been at the dancing-school, had to dance and be admired again by her mother. What with kissing, and dancing, and being wept over, the little Kenwigses had a very busy evening, and were the life of the party.

THE CHILD'S STORY

XVI

THE CHILD'S STORY

ONCE upon a time, a good many years ago, there was a traveller, and he set out upon a journey. It was a magic journey, and was to seem very long when he began it, and very short when he got half-way through.

He travelled along a rather dark path for some little time without meeting anything, until at last he came to a beautiful child. So he said to the child: "What do you do here?" And the child said: "I am always at play. Come and play with me!"

So he played with that child the whole day long, and they were very merry. The sky was so blue, the sun was so bright, the water was so sparkling, the leaves were so green, the flowers were so lovely, and they heard such singing birds, and saw so many butterflies, that everything was beautiful. This was in fine weather. When it rained, they loved to watch the falling drops, and to smell the fresh scents. When it blew, it was delightful to listen to the wind, and fancy what it said, as it came rushing from its home — where was that, they wondered! — whistling and howling, driving the clouds before it, bending the trees, rumbling in the chimneys, shaking the house, and making the sea roar in fury. But when it snowed, that was best of all; for they liked nothing so well as to look up at the white flakes falling fast and thick, like down from the breasts of millions of white birds; and to see how smooth and deep the drift was; and to listen to the hush upon the paths and roads.

They had plenty of the finest toys in the world, and the most astonishing picture-books: all about scimitars and slippers and turbans, and dwarfs and giants and genii and fairies, and blue-beards and bean-stalks and riches and caverns, and forests and Valentines and Orsons: and all new and all true.

But one day, of a sudden, the traveller lost the child. He called to him over and over again, but got no answer. So he went upon his road, and went on for a little while without meeting anything, until at last he came to a handsome boy. So he said to the boy, "What do you do here?" And the boy said: "I am always learning. Come and learn with me."

So he learned with that boy about Jupiter and Juno, and the Greeks and the Romans, and I don't know what, and learned more than I could tell — or he either, for he soon forgot a deal of it. But they were not always learning; they had the merriest games that ever were played. They rowed upon the river in summer, and skated on the ice in winter; they were active afoot, and active on horseback; at cricket, and all games at ball; at prisoners' base, hare and hounds, follow my leader, and more sports than I can think of; nobody could beat them. They had holidays, too, and Twelfth cakes, and parties where they danced till midnight, and real theatres where they saw palaces of real gold and silver rise out of the real earth, and saw all the wonders of the world at once. As to friends, they had such dear friends, and so many of them, that I want the time to reckon them up. They were all young, like the handsome boy, and were never to be strange to one another all their lives through.

Still, one day, in the midst of all these pleasures, the traveller lost the boy as he had lost the child, and, after calling to him in vain, went on upon his journey. So he went on for a little while without seeing anything, until at last he came to a young man. So he said to the young man: "What do you do here?" And the young man said: "I am always in love. Come and love with me?"

So he went away with that young man, and presently they came to one of the prettiest girls that ever was seen — just like Fanny in the corner there — and she had eyes like Fanny, and hair like Fanny, and dimples like Fanny's, and she laughed and colored just as Fanny does while I am talking about her. So the young man fell in love directly — just as Somebody I won't mention, the first time he came here, did with Fanny. Well! he was teased sometimes — just as Somebody used to be by Fanny; and they quarrelled sometimes — just as Somebody and Fanny used to quarrel; and they made it up, and sat in the dark, and wrote letters every day, and never were happy asunder, and were always looking out for one another and pretending not to, and were engaged at Christmas time, and sat close to one another by the fire, and were going to be married very soon — all exactly like Somebody I won't mention, and Fanny!

[159]

But the traveller lost them one day, as he had lost the rest of his friends, and, after calling to them to come back, which they never did, went on upon his journey. So he went on for a little while without seeing anything, until at last he came to a middle-aged gentleman. So he said to the gentleman, "What are you doing here?" And his answer was: "I am always busy. Come and be busy with me!"

So he began to be very busy with that gentleman, and they went on through the wood together. The whole journey was through a wood, only it had been open and green at first, like a wood in spring; and now began to be thick and dark, like a wood in summer; some of the little trees that had come out earliest were even turning brown. The gentleman was not alone, but had a lady of about the same age with him, who was his wife; and they had children, who were with them too. So they all went on together through the wood, cutting down the trees, and making a path through the branches and the fallen leaves, and carrying burdens, and working hard.

Sometimes, they came to a long green avenue that opened into deeper woods. Then they would hear a very little distant voice crying: "Father, father, I am another child! Stop for me!" And presently they would see a very little figure, growing larger as it came along, running to join them. When it came up, they all crowded round it, and kissed and welcomed it; and then they all went on together.

Sometimes, they came to several avenues at once, and then they all stood still, and one of the children said: "Father,

THE CHILD'S STORY

I am going to sea," and another said, "Father, I am going to India," and another, "Father, I am going to seek my fortune where I can," and another, "Father, I am going to Heaven!" So, with many tears at parting, they went, solitary, down those avenues, each child upon its way; and the child who went to Heaven rose into the golden air and vanished.

Whenever these partings happened, the traveller looked at the gentleman, and saw him glance up at the sky above the trees, where the day was beginning to decline, and the sunset to come on. He saw, too, that his hair was turning gray. But they never could rest long, for they had their journey to perform, and it was necessary for them to be always busy.

At last, there had been so many partings that there were no children left, and only the traveller, the gentleman, and the lady, went upon their way in company. And now the wood was yellow; and now brown; and the leaves, even of the forest trees, began to fall.

So they came to an avenue that was darker than the rest, and were pressing forward on their journey without looking down it when the lady stopped.

"My husband," said the lady. "I am called."

They listened, and they heard a voice a long way down the avenue say: "Mother, mother!"

It was the voice of the first child who had said: "I am going to Heaven!" and the father said, "I pray not yet. The sunset is very near. I pray not yet!"

But the voice cried: "Mother, mother!" without minding

him, though his hair was now quite white, and tears were on his face.

Then the mother, who was already drawn into the shade of the dark avenue and moving away with her arms still round his neck, kissed him, and said: "My dearest, I am summoned, and I go!" And she was gone. And the traveller and he were left alone together.

And they went on and on together, until they came to very near the end of the wood: so near, that they could see the sunset shining red before them through the trees.

Yet, once more, while he broke his way among the branches, the traveller lost his friend. He called and called, but there was no reply, and when he passed out of the wood and saw the peaceful sun going down upon a wide purple prospect, he came to an old man sitting on a fallen tree. So he said to the old man: "What do you do here?" And the old man said with a calm smile: "I am always remembering. Come and remember with me!"

So the traveller sat down by the side of that old man, face to face with the serene sunset; and all his friends came softly back and stood around him. The beautiful child, the handsome boy, the young man in love, the father, mother, and children; every one of them was there, and he had lost nothing. So he loved them all, and was kind and forbearing with them all, and was always pleased to watch them all, and they all honored and loved him. And I think the traveller must be yourself, dear grandfather, because this is what you do to us, and what we do to you.

THE BOY AT TODGERS'S

XVII

THE BOY AT TODGERS'S

WHEN Mr. Pecksniff and his two daughters came to London, they found their way to Mrs. Todgers's Boarding House. It was early in the morning and they rang two or three times without making any impression on anything but a dog over the way. At last a chain and some bolts were withdrawn, and a small boy with a large red head, and no nose to speak of, and a pair of huge boots under his arm, appeared. The boy rubbed his nose with the back of his shoe brush and said nothing.

"Still abed, my man?" asked Mr. Pecksniff.

"Still abed!" replied the boy, "I wish they wos still abed. They're very noisy abed, all calling for their boots at once. I thought you was the Paper and wondered why you didn't shove yourself through the grating as usual. What do you want?"

The boy was called Bailey, and though he was a little cross when the Pecksniffs came because it was so early in the morning, he was usually the soul of good humor. Indeed, good humor was about the only thing he had, for no one had taken the trouble to teach him good manners.

Bailey would roll up his sleeves to the shoulders and find

his way all over the house, and wherever he went he made things lively. He wore an apron of coarse green baize. He would answer the door and then make a bolt for the alley, and in a moment be playing leap-frog, till Mrs. Todgers followed him and pulled him into the house by the hair of his head.

When the two Miss Pecksniffs were sitting primly on the sofa, Bailey would greet them with such compliments as: "There you are agin! Ain't it nice!" This made them feel very much at home.

"I say," he whispered, stopping in one of his journeys to and fro, "young ladies, there's soup to-morrow. She's making it now. Ain't she putting in the water? Oh! not at all neither!"

The next time he passed by he called out:

"I say — there's fowls to-morrow. Not skinny ones. Oh, no!"

Presently he called through the key-hole:

"There's a fish to-morrow — just come. Don't eat none of him!" And, with this warning, he vanished again.

. . . .

By-and-by, he returned to lay the cloth for supper, it having been arranged between Mrs. Todgers and the young ladies that they should partake of an exclusive veal-cutlet together in the privacy of that apartment. He entertained them on this occasion by thrusting the lighted candle into his mouth, and exhibiting his face in a state of transparency; after the performance of which feat he went on with his professional duties; brightening every knife as he laid it on the table, by breathing on the blade and afterward polishing the same on the apron already mentioned. When he had completed his preparations, he grinned at the sisters, and expressed his belief that the approaching collation would be of "rather a spicy sort."

"Will it be long before it's ready, Bailey?" asked Mercy.

"No," said Bailey, "it *is* cooked. When I come up, she was dodging among the tender pieces with a fork, and eating of 'em."

But he had scarcely achieved the utterance of these words, when he received a manual compliment on the head, which sent him staggering against the wall; and Mrs. Todgers, dish in hand, stood indignantly before him.

"Oh, you little villain!" said that lady. "Oh, you bad, false boy!"

"No worse than yerself," retorted Bailey, guarding his head, in a principle invented by Mr. Thomas Cribb. "Ah! Come now! Do that agin, will yer!"

"He's the most dreadful child," said Mrs. Todgers, setting down the dish, "I ever had to deal with. The gentlemen spoil him to that extent, and teach him such things, that I'm afraid nothing but hanging will ever do him any good."

"Won't it?" cried Bailey. "Oh! Yes! Wot do you go a lowerin' the table-beer for then, and destroying my constitooshun?"

"Go down-stairs, you vicious boy," said Mrs. Todgers, holding the door open. "Do you hear me? Go along!"

THE CHILDREN OF DICKENS

After two or three dexterous feints, he went, and was seen no more that night, save once, when he brought up some tumblers and hot water, and much disturbed the two Miss Pecksniffs by squinting hideously behind the back of the unconscious Mrs. Todgers. Having done this justice to his wounded feelings, he returned underground; whence, in company with a swarm of black beetles and a kitchen candle, he employed his faculties in cleaning boots and brushing clothes until the night was far advanced.

.   .   .   .

But it was at the Sunday dinner that Bailey shone in glory. When the hour drew near, he appeared in a complete suit of cast-off clothes several times too large for him, and a clean shirt of extraordinary size. This caused the boarders to call him "Collars." Then Bailey would announce joyfully: "The wittles is up."

When all were seated, Bailey would stand behind the chair winking and nodding with the greatest good humor. His idea of waiting on the table was to stand with his hands in his pockets and his feet wide apart. This was on the whole the best thing to do, for when a dish passed through his hands it was quite likely to drop on the floor.

Mrs. Todgers was always scolding Bailey, who deserved it all, and Bailey was always threatening to leave and be a soldier boy.

"There's something gamey in that, ain't there? I'd sooner be hit with a cannon-ball than a rolling-pin, and she's always a catching up something of that sort and throwing it at me, when the gentlemen's appetites is good. But I ain't going to have every rise in prices wisited on me."

Mrs. Todgers got rid of Bailey after a while, but the boarders never got the same amount of amusement from his successor. The house always seemed a little dull after he left.

THE DOMBEY CHILDREN

PAUL DOMBEY AND FLORENCE ON THE BEACH AT BRIGHTON

XVIII

THE DOMBEY CHILDREN

IN London there is a portion of the huge town that is called the City. People do not live in the City — they do business there. That is where the big banks are and the offices of the great merchants whose ships go round the world. In the City the Lord Mayor of London rules, as he did in the days when the gay apprentice, Dick Whittington, heard the bells prophesying what he should be.

On one of the streets of the City was a building that had an ancient sign, Dombey and Son. It had been there many years, since the time when the original Dombey had taken his son into partnership. The Dombeys owned a great many ships that sailed to the West Indies and the East Indies, and wherever they could make money on their voyages. Up to this time, each Dombey had been a good business man and had taught his son how to save and how to venture wisely. So that the Dombeys had become richer and richer. All had gone well with them; but there had come a time when there was a Dombey who hadn't any son. Mr. and Mrs. Dombey had a daughter named Florence, who was a very nice little girl. Her mother loved her dearly, but her father thought she didn't amount to much, because he couldn't put on the sign on his office the words, "Dombey and Daughter." That wouldn't have sounded right in the days of good **Queen Victoria**. He wanted the name to be always Dombey and Son.

When at last a boy was born, Mr. Dombey was delighted. He dreamed of a time when little Paul would grow up to be a man just like himself, and would take his place in the office and make everybody afraid of him. He should be the Prince while his father was King in the Kingdom of Dombey and Son. All this was very pleasant to think about, and it seemed as if the business in the City would go on forever. But while Mr. Dombey dreamed of what his son would do when he was grown up, he didn't do anything to help him grow. Paul was a poor little rich boy, who lived in a big, uncomfortable house, and was sent to school with other poor little rich boys. I'm sorry for little Paul, but I don't care to read about him very much

It's a relief to meet the people who didn't have any money, for they seem so much more cheerful than any of the Dombeys. There was Toodles, the husband of little Paul's nurse. Mr. Dombey wanted to find out all about him.

"Mr. What's-your-name, you have a son, I believe."

"Four on 'em, sir. Four hims and a her. All alive."

"Why, it's as much as you can afford to keep them!" said Mr. Dombey.

"I couldn't afford but one thing in the world less, sir."

"What is that?"

"To lose 'em, sir."

"Can you read?" asked Mr. Dombey.

"Why, not partik'ler, sir."

"Write?"

"With chalk, sir?"

"With anything."

"I could make shift to chalk a bit, I think, if I were put to it," said Toodles after some reflection.

"And yet," said Mr. Dombey, "you are two or three-and-thirty, I suppose."

"Thereabouts, I suppose, sir," answered Toodles after more reflection.

"Then why don't you learn?" asked Mr. Dombey.

"So I'm agoing to, sir. One of my little boys is agoing to learn me when he's old enough, and been to school himself."

"Well!" said Mr. Dombey. It was all that he could say. It all seemed so foolish. It would have surprised Mr. Dombey if he had been told that Mr. Toodles's children were more fortunate than his own, and that they were having a great deal better time. But that was what Dickens thought, and I agree with him.

Little Paul was so carefully looked after that he had no adventures. But his sister Florence had better luck. One of her adventures was quite exciting, for she was lost in one of the worst parts of London, and was rescued by a young gentleman who felt the romance of it. At the time Paul was a baby, and Mrs. Toodles had a longing to see her own children. So without asking permission she took Paul and Florence with her. They found their way to the poor part of town where her family lived, and all the little Toodleses greeted their mother with shouts, and there was a great celebration. On going home they fell in with a noisy and pushing crowd. Mrs. Toodles of course looked after little Paul, who was very important, but she forgot Florence for a moment. When she looked for her she wasn't there. What followed let Dickens tell.

HOW FLORENCE DOMBEY WAS LOST IN LONDON

AS Susan Nipper and the two children were in the crowd, there came a wild cry of "Mad bull!" With a wild confusion before her, of people running up and down, and shouting, and wheels running over them, and boys fighting, and mad bulls coming up, and the nurse in the midst of all these dangers being torn to pieces, Florence screamed and ran. She ran till she was exhausted, urging Susan to do the same; and then, stopping and wringing her hands as she remembered they had left the other nurse behind, found, with a sensation of terror not to be described, that she was quite alone.

"Susan! Susan!" cried Florence, clapping her hands in the very ecstasy of her alarm. "Oh, where are they! where are they!"

"Where are they?" said an old woman, coming hobbling across as fast as she could from the opposite side of the way. "Why did you run away from 'em?"

"I was frightened," answered Florence. "I didn't know what I did. I thought they were with me. Where are they?"

THE DOMBEY CHILDREN

The old woman took her by the wrist, and said: "I'll show you."

She was a very ugly old woman, with red rims round her eyes, and a mouth that mumbled and chattered of itself when she was not speaking. She was miserably dressed, and carried some skins over her arm. She seemed to have followed Florence some little way at all events, for she had lost her breath; and this made her uglier still, as she stood trying to regain it: working her shrivelled, yellow face and throat into all sorts of contortions.

Florence was afraid of her, and looked, hesitating, up the street, of which she had almost reached the bottom. It was a solitary place — more a back road than a street — and there was no one in it but herself and the old woman.

"You needn't be frightened now," said the old woman, still holding her tight. "Come along with me."

"I — I don't know you. What's your name?" asked Florence.

"Mrs. Brown," said the old woman. "Good Mrs. Brown."

"Are they near here?" asked Florence, beginning to be led away.

"Susan an't far off," said Good Mrs. Brown; "and the others are close to her."

"Is anybody hurt?" cried Florence.

"Not a bit of it," said Good Mrs. Brown.

The child shed tears of delight on hearing this, and accompanied the old woman willingly; though she could not help glancing at her face as they went along — particularly at that industrious mouth — and wondering whether Bad Mrs. Brown, if there were such a person, was at all like her

They had not gone very far, but had gone by some very uncomfortable places, such as brick-fields and tile-yards, when the old woman turned down a dirty lane, where the mud lay in deep black ruts in the middle of the road. She stopped before a shabby little house, as closely shut up as a house that was full of cracks and crevices could be. Opening the door with a key she took out of her bonnet, she pushed the child before her into a back room, where there was a great heap of rags of different colors lying on the floor; a heap of bones, and a heap of sifted dust or cinders; but there was no furniture at all, and the walls and ceiling were quite black.

The child became so terrified that she was stricken speechless, and looked as though about to swoon.

"Now don't be a young mule," said Good Mrs. Brown, reviving her with a shake. "I'm not a going to hurt you. Sit upon the rags."

Florence obeyed her, holding out her folded hands, in mute supplication.

"I'm not a going to keep you, even, above an hour," said Mrs. Brown. "D'ye understand what I say?"

The child answered with great difficulty, "Yes."

"Then," said Good Mrs. Brown, taking her own seat on the bones, "don't vex me. If you don't, I tell you I won't hurt you. But if you do, I'll kill you. I could have you killed at any time — even if you was in your own bed at home. Now let's know who you are, and what you are, and all about it."

The old woman's threats and promises; the dread of giving her offense; and the habit, unusual to a child, but almost natural to Florence now, of being quiet, and repressing what she felt, and feared, and hoped, enabled her to do this bidding, and to tell her little history, or what she knew of it. Mrs. Brown listened attentively, until she had finished.

"So your name's Dombey, eh?" said Mrs. Brown.

"Yes, ma'am."

"I want that pretty frock, Miss Dombey," said Good Mrs. Brown, "and that little bonnet, and a petticoat or two, and anything else you can spare. Come! Take 'em off."

Florence obeyed, as fast as her trembling hands would allow; keeping, all the while, a frightened eye on Mrs. Brown. When she had divested herself of all the articles of apparel mentioned by that lady, Mrs. B. examined them at leisure, and seemed tolerably well satisfied with their quality and value.

"Humph!" she said, running her eyes over the child's slight figure. "I don't see anything else — except the shoes. I must have the shoes, Miss Dombey."

Poor little Florence took them off with equal alacrity, only too glad to have any more means of conciliation about her. The old woman then produced some wretched substitutes from the bottom of the heap of rags, which she turned up for that purpose; together with a girl's cloak, quite worn out and very old; and the crushed remains of a bonnet that had probably been picked up from some ditch or dunghill. In this dainty raiment, she instructed Florence to dress herself; and as such preparation seemed a prelude to her release, the child complied with increased readiness, if possible.

In hurriedly putting on the bonnet, if that may be called a bonnet which was more like a pad to carry loads on, she caught it in her hair which grew luxuriantly, and could not immediately disentangle it. Good Mrs. Brown whipped out a large pair of scissors, and fell into an unaccountable state of excitement.

"Why couldn't you let me be!" said Mrs. Brown "when I was contented. You little fool!"

"I beg your pardon. I don't know what I have done," panted Florence. "I couldn't help it."

"Couldn't help it!" cried Mrs. Brown. "How do you expect I can help it? Why, Lord!" said the old woman, ruffling her curls with a furious pleasure, "anybody but me would have had 'em off, first of all."

Florence was so relieved to find that it was only her hair and not her head which Mrs. Brown coveted, that she offered no resistance or entreaty, and merely raised her mild eyes toward the face of that good soul.

"If I hadn't once had a gal of my own — beyond seas now — that was proud of her hair," said Mrs. Brown, "I'd have had every lock of it. She's far away, she's far away! Oho! Oho!"

Mrs. Brown's was not a melodious cry, but, accompanied with a wild tossing up of her lean arms, it was full of passionate grief, and thrilled to the heart of Florence, whom it frightened more than ever. It had its part, perhaps, in saving her curls; for Mrs. Brown, after hovering about her with the scissors for some moments, like a new kind of butterfly, bade her hide them under the bonnet and let no trace of them escape to tempt her. Having accomplished this victory over herself, Mrs. Brown resumed her seat on the bones, and smoked a very short black pipe, mowing and mumbling all the time, as if she were eating the stem.

When the pipe was smoked out, she gave the child a rabbit-skin to carry, that she might appear the more like her ordinary companion, and told her that she was now going to lead her to a public street, whence she could inquire her way to her friends. But she cautioned her, with threats of summary and deadly vengeance in case of disobedience, not to talk to strangers, nor to repair to her own home (which may have been too near for Mrs. Brown's convenience), but to her father's office in the City; also to wait at the street corner where she would be left, until the clock struck three. These directions Mrs. Brown enforced with assurances that there would be potent eyes and ears in her employment cognizant of all she did; and these directions Florence promised faithfully and earnestly to observe.

At length, Mrs. Brown, issuing forth, conducted her changed and ragged little friend through a labyrinth of narrow streets and lanes and alleys, which emerged, after a long time, upon a stable-yard, with a gateway at the end, whence the roar of a great thoroughfare made itself audible. Pointing out this gateway, and informing Florence that when the clocks struck three she was to go to the left, Mrs. Brown, after making a parting grasp at her hair which seemed involuntary and quite beyond her own control, told her she knew what to do, and bade her go and do it: remembering that she was watched.

With a lighter heart, but still sore afraid, Florence felt herself released, and tripped off to the corner. When she reached it, she looked back and saw the head of Good Mrs. Brown peeping out of the low wooden passage, where she had issued her parting injunctions; likewise the fist of Good Mrs. Brown shaking toward her. But though she often looked back afterward — every minute, at least, in her nervous recollection of the old woman — she could not see her again.

Florence remained there, looking at the bustle in the street, and more and more bewildered by it; and in the meanwhile the clocks appeared to have made up their minds never to strike three any more. At last the steeples rang out three o'clock; there was one close by, so she couldn't be mistaken; and — after often looking over her shoulder, and often going a little way, and as often coming back again, lest the all-powerful spies of Mrs. Brown should take offense — she hurried off, as fast as she could in her slipshod shoes, holding the rabbit-skin tight in her hand.

All she knew of her father's offices was that they belonged to Dombey and Son, and that that was a great power belonging to the City. So she could only ask the way to Dom-

bey and Son's in the City; and as she generally made inquiry
of children — being afraid to ask grown people — she got
very little satisfaction indeed. But by dint of asking her
way to the City after a while, and dropping the rest of her
inquiry for the present, she really did advance, by slow degrees, toward the heart of that great region which is governed by the terrible Lord Mayor.

Tired of walking, repulsed and pushed about, stunned by
the noise and confusion, anxious for her brother and the
nurses, terrified by what she had undergone, and the prospect of encountering her angry father in such an altered state;
perplexed and frightened alike by what had passed, and
what was passing, and what was yet before her, Florence
went upon her weary way with tearful eyes, and once or
twice could not help stopping to ease her bursting heart by
crying bitterly. But few people noticed her at those times,
in the garb she wore; or if they did, believed that she was
tutored to excite compassion, and passed on. Florence, too,
called to her aid all the firmness and self-reliance of a character that her sad experience had prematurely formed and
tried; and keeping the end she had in view steadily before
her, steadily pursued it.

It was full two hours later in the afternoon than when
she had started on this strange adventure, when, escaping
from the clash and clangor of a narrow street full of carts
and wagons, she peeped into a kind of wharf or landing-
place upon the riverside, where there were a great many
packages, casks, and boxes strewn about; a large pair of

wooden scales; and a little wooden house on wheels, outside of which, looking at the neighboring masts and boats, a stout man stood whistling, with his pen behind his ear, and his hands in his pockets, as if his day's work were nearly done.

"Now then!" said this man, happening to turn round. "We haven't got anything for you, little girl. Be off!"

"If you please, is this the City?" asked the trembling daughter of the Dombeys.

"Ah! it's the City. You know that well enough, I dare say. Be off! We haven't got anything for you."

"I don't want anything, thank you," was the timid answer. "Except to know the way to Dombey and Son's."

The man who had been strolling carelessly toward her, seemed surprised by this reply, and looking attentively in her face, rejoined:

"Why, what can *you* want with Dombey and Son's?"

"To know the way there, if you please."

The man looked at her yet more curiously, and rubbed the back of his head so hard in his wonderment that he knocked his own hat off.

"Joe!" he called to another man — a laborer — as he picked it up and put it on again.

"Joe it is!" said Joe.

"Where's that young spark of Dombey's who's been watching the shipment of them goods?"

"Just gone, by the t'other gate," said Joe.

"Call him back a minute."

THE DOMBEY CHILDREN

Joe ran up an archway, bawling as he went, and very soon returned with a blithe-looking boy.

"You're Dombey's jockey, an't you?" said the first man.

"I'm in Dombey's House, Mr. Clark," returned the boy.

"Look ye here, then," said Mr. Clark.

Obedient to the indication of Mr. Clark's hand, the boy approached toward Florence, wondering, as well he might, what he had to do with her. But she, who had heard what passed, and who, besides the relief of so suddenly considering herself safe at her journey's end, felt reassured beyond all measure by his lively youthful face and manner, ran eagerly up to him, leaving one of the slipshod shoes upon the ground and caught his hand in both of hers.

"I am lost, if you please!" said Florence.

"Lost!" cried the boy.

"Yes, I was lost this morning, a long way from here — and I have had my clothes taken away, since — and I am not dressed in my own now — and my name is Florence Dombey, my little brother's only sister — and, oh dear, dear, take care of me, if you please!" sobbed Florence, giving full vent to the childish feelings she had so long suppressed, and bursting into tears. At the same time her miserable bonnet falling off, her hair came tumbling down about her face: moving to speechless admiration and commiseration, young Walter, nephew of Solomon Gills, ships' instrument-maker in general.

Mr. Clark stood rapt in amazement: observing under his breath, *I* never saw such a start on *this* wharf before. Walter picked up the shoe, and put it on the little foot as the Prince in the story might have fitted Cinderella's slipper on. He hung the rabbit-skin over his left arm; gave the right to Florence; and felt, not to say like Richard Whittington — that is a tame comparison — but like Saint George of England, with the dragon lying dead before him.

"Don't cry, Miss Dombey," said Walter, in a transport of enthusiasm. "What a wonderful thing for me that I am here. You are as safe now as if you were guarded by a whole boat's crew of picked men from a man-of-war. Oh, don't cry."

"I won't cry any more," said Florence. "I am only crying for joy."

"Crying for joy!" thought Walter, "and I'm the cause of it! Come along, Miss Dombey. There's the other shoe off now! Take mine, Miss Dombey."

"No, no, no," said Florence, checking him in the act of impetuously pulling off his own. "These do better. These do very well."

"Why, to be sure," said Walter, glancing at her foot, "mine are a mile too large. What am I thinking about! You never could walk in *mine!* Come along, Miss Dombey. Let me see the villain who will dare molest you now."

So Walter, looking immensely fierce, led off Florence, looking very happy; and they went arm in arm along the streets, perfectly indifferent to any astonishment that their appearance might or did excite by the way.

.   .   .   .

[186]

Then, though it was growing dark and foggy, Florence was perfectly happy, and Walter felt that he was a knight escorting a princess to her father's castle.

PAUL DOMBEY AT BRIGHTON

LITTLE Paul Dombey was only six and very small for his age, when his father sent him to a boarding-school at Brighton. The head master's name was Blimber, and he prided himself on giving information to his pupils at all times. Here is a scene at the dinner table.

.   .   .   .   `   .

Doctor Blimber was already in his place in the dining-room, at the top of the table, with Miss Blimber and Mrs. Blimber on either side of him. Mr. Feeder in a black coat was at the bottom. Paul's chair was next to Miss Blimber; but it being found, when he sat in it, that his eyebrows were not much above the level of the table-cloth, some books were brought in from the Doctor's study, on which he was elevated, and on which he always sat from that time — carrying them in and out himself on after occasions, like a little elephant and castle.

Grace having been said by the Doctor, dinner began. There was some nice soup; also roast meat, boiled meat, vegetables, pie, and cheese. Every young gentleman had a massive silver fork, and a napkin; and all the arrangements were stately and handsome. In particular, there was a butler in a blue coat and bright buttons, who gave quite a winey flavor to the table beer; he poured it out so superbly.

Nobody spoke, unless spoken to, except Doctor Blimber, Mrs. Blimber, and Miss Blimber, who conversed occasionally. Whenever a young gentleman was not actually engaged with his knife and fork or spoon, his eye, with an irresistible attraction, sought the eye of Doctor Blimber, Mrs. Blimber, or Miss Blimber, and modestly rested there. Toots appeared to be the only exception to this rule. He sat next Mr. Feeder on Paul's side of the table, and frequently looked behind and before the intervening boys to catch a glimpse of Paul.

Only once during dinner was there any conversation that included the young gentlemen. It happened at the epoch of the cheese, when the Doctor, having taken a glass of port wine and hemmed twice or thrice, said:

"It is remarkable, Mr. Feeder, that the Romans —— "

At the mention of this terrible people, their implacable enemies, every young gentleman fastened his gaze upon the Doctor, with an assumption of the deepest interest. One of the number who happened to be drinking, and who caught the Doctor's eye glaring at him through the side of his tumbler, left off so hastily that he was convulsed for some moments, and in the sequel ruined Doctor Blimber's point.

"It is remarkable, Mr. Feeder," said the Doctor, beginning again slowly, "that the Romans, in those gorgeous and profuse entertainments of which we read in the days of the

Emperors, when luxury had attained a height unknown before or since, and when whole provinces were ravaged to supply the splendid means of one Imperial Banquet —— "

Here the offender, who had been swelling and straining, and waiting in vain for a full stop, broke out violently.

"Johnson," said Mr. Feeder, in a low, reproachful voice, "take some water."

The Doctor, looking very stern, made a pause until the water was brought, and then resumed:

"And when, Mr. Feeder —— "

But Mr. Feeder, who saw that Johnson must break out again, and who knew that the Doctor would never come to a period before the young gentlemen until he had finished all he meant to say, couldn't keep his eye off Johnson; and thus was caught in the act of not looking at the Doctor, who consequently stopped.

"I beg your pardon, sir," said Mr. Feeder, reddening. "I beg your pardon, Doctor Blimber."

"And when," said the Doctor, raising his voice, "when, sir, as we read, and have no reason to doubt — incredible as it may appear to the vulgar of our time — the brother of Vitellius prepared for him a feast, in which were served, of fish, two thousand dishes —— "

"Take some water, Johnson — dishes, sir," said Mr. Feeder.

"Of various sorts of fowl, five thousand dishes."

"Or try a crust of bread," said Mr. Feeder.

"And one dish," pursued Doctor Blimber, raising his

voice still higher as he looked all round the table, "called, from its enormous dimensions, the Shield of Minerva, and made, among other costly ingredients, of the brains of pheasants —— "

"Ow, ow, ow!" (from Johnson).

"Woodcocks, —— "

"Ow, ow, ow!"

"The sounds of the fish called scari, —— "

"You'll burst some vessel in your head," said Mr. Feeder. "You had better let it come."

"And the spawn of the lamprey, brought from the Carpathian Sea," pursued the Doctor, in his severest voice; "when we read of costly entertainments such as these, and still remember, that we have a Titus, —— "

"What would be your mother's feelings if you died of apoplexy!" said Mr. Feeder.

"A Domitian, —— "

"And you're blue, you know," said Mr. Feeder.

"A Nero, a Tiberius, a Caligula, a Heliogabalus, and many more," pursued the Doctor; "it is, Mr. Feeder — if you are doing me the honor to attend — remarkable; VERY remarkable, sir —— "

But Johnson, unable to suppress it any longer, burst at that moment into such an overwhelming fit of coughing, that, although both his immediate neighbors thumped him on the back, and Mr. Feeder himself held a glass of water to his lips, and the butler walked him up and down several times between his own chair and the sideboard, like a sentry, it was full five minutes before he was moderately composed. Then there was a profound silence.

"Gentlemen," said Doctor Blimber, "rise for grace! Cornelia, lift Dombey down" — nothing of whom but his scalp was accordingly seen above the table-cloth. "Johnson will repeat to me to-morrow morning before breakfast, without book, and from the Greek Testament, the first Epistle of Saint Paul to the Ephesians. We will resume our studies, Mr. Feeder, in half-an-hour."

.   .   .   .

No wonder that poor little Paul looked forward longingly to the happy Saturdays, for then Florence always came at noon, and they had long walks on the great beach, and watched the waves come in. Then Paul forgot about Doctor Blimber and Nero, and Tiberius and the rest, and only knew how much he loved his sister.

JEMMY JACKMAN LIRRIPER'S STORY

XIX

JEMMY JACKMAN LIRRIPER'S STORY

MRS. LIRRIPER kept a lodging-house at 81 Norfolk Street, London. Major Jackman was one of the lodgers, and a very kindly gentleman he was. One day a young woman left Jemmy at the house, and Mrs. Lirriper adopted him as her grandchild, and when he was christened the Major stood as godfather. Jemmy grew up to be a fine boy, and was sent to school in Lincolnshire. Mrs. Lirriper and the Major were very lonely while he was away, and there was great rejoicing when he came back for the Christmas holidays. They sat by the Christmas fire and told stories. The Major afterward repeated Jemmy's story thus.

.   .   .   .

Our first reunited Christmas Day was the most delightful one we have ever passed together. Jemmy was never silent for five minutes, except in church-time. He talked as we sat by the fire, he talked when we were out walking, he talked as we sat by the fire again, he talked incessantly at dinner, though he made a dinner almost as remarkable as himself. It was the spring of happiness in his fresh young heart flowing and flowing, and it fertilized (if I may be allowed so bold a figure) my much-esteemed friend, and J. J. the present writer.

[195]

THE CHILDREN OF DICKENS

There were only we three. We dined, in my esteemed friend's little room, and our entertainment was perfect. But everything in the establishment is, in neatness, order, and comfort, always perfect. After dinner our boy slipped away to his old stool at my esteemed friend's knee, and there, with his hot chestnuts and his glass of brown sherry (really, a most excellent wine!) on a chair for a table, his face out-shone the apples in the dish.

We talked of these jottings of mine, which Jemmy had read through and through by that time; and so it came about that my esteemed friend remarked, as she sat smoothing Jemmy's curls:

"And as you belong to the house too, Jemmy, — and so much more than the lodgers, having been born in it, — why your story ought to be added to the rest I think, one of these days."

Jemmy's eyes sparkled at this, and he said: "So I think, Gran."

Then he sat looking at the fire, and then he began to laugh in a sort of confidence with the fire, and then he said, folding his arms across my esteemed friend's lap, and raising his bright face to hers: "Would you like to hear a boy's story, Gran?"

"Of all things," replied my esteemed friend.

"Would you, Godfather?"

"Of all things," I too replied.

"Well, then," said Jemmy, "I'll tell you one."

Here our indisputably remarkable boy gave himself a

hug, and laughed again, musically, at the idea of his coming out in that new line. Then he once more took the fire into the same sort of confidence as before, and began:

"Once upon a time, When pigs drank wine, And monkeys chewed tobaccer, 'Twas neither in your time nor mine, But that's no macker —— "

"Bless the child!" cried my esteemed friend, "what's amiss with his brain?"

"It's poetry, Gran," returned Jemmy, shouting with laughter. "We always begin stories that way at school."

"Gave me quite a turn, Major," said my esteemed friend, fanning herself with a plate. "Thought he was light-headed!"

"In those remarkable times, Gran and Godfather, there was once a boy, — not me, you know."

"No, no," says my respected friend, "not you. Not him, Major, you understand?"

"No, no," says I.

"And he went to school in Rutlandshire —— "

"Why not Lincolnshire?" says my respected friend.

"Why not, you dear old gran? Because *I* go to school in Lincolnshire, don't I?"

"Ah, to be sure!" says my respected friend. "And it's not Jemmy, you understand, Major?"

"No, no," says I.

"Well!" our boy proceeded, hugging himself comfortably, and laughing merrily (again in confidence with the fire), before he again looked up in Mrs. Lirriper's face, "and so he was tremendously in love with his schoolmaster's daughter, and she was the most beautiful creature that ever was seen, and she had brown eyes, and she had brown hair all curling beautifully, and she had a delicious voice, and she was delicious altogether, and her name was Seraphina."

"What's the name of *your* schoolmaster's daughter, Jemmy?" asks my respected friend.

"Polly!" replied Jemmy, pointing his forefinger at her. "There now! Caught you! Ha, ha, ha!"

When he and my respected friend had had a laugh and a hug together, our admittedly remarkable boy resumed with a great relish:

"Well! And so he loved her. And so he thought about her, and dreamed about her, and made her presents of oranges and nuts, and would have made her presents of pearls and diamonds if he could have afforded it out of his pocket-money, but he couldn't. And so her father — Oh, he WAS a Tartar! Keeping the boys up to the mark, holding examinations once a month, lecturing upon all sorts of subjects at all sorts of times, and knowing everything in the world out of book. And so this boy —— "

"Had he any name?" asks my respected friend.

"No, he hadn't, Gran. Ha, ha! There now! Caught you again!"

After this, they had another laugh and another hug, and then our boy went on.

"Well! And so this boy, he had a friend about as old as himself at the same school, and his name (for he *had* a name, as it happened) was — let me remember — was Bobbo."

[198]

"Not Bob," says my respected friend.

"Of course not," says Jemmy. "What made you think it was, Gran? Well! And so this friend was the cleverest and bravest and best-looking and most generous of all the friends that ever were, and so he was in love with Seraphina's sister, and so Seraphina's sister was in love with him, and so they all grew up."

"Bless us!" says my respected friend. "They were very sudden about it."

"So they all grew up," our boy repeated, laughing heartily, "and Bobbo and this boy went away together on horseback to seek their fortunes, and they partly got their horses by favor, and partly in a bargain; that is to say, they had saved up between them seven and fourpence, and the two horses, being Arabs, were worth more, only the man said he would take that, to favor them. Well! And so they made their fortunes and came prancing back to the school, with their pockets full of gold, enough to last forever. And so they rang at the parents' and visitors' bell (not the back gate), and when the bell was answered they proclaimed 'The same as if it was scarlet fever! Every boy goes home for an indefinite period!' And then there was great hurrahing, and then they kissed Seraphina and her sister, — each his own love, and not the other's on any account, — and then they ordered the Tartar into instant confinement."

"Poor man!" said my respected friend.

"Into instant confinement, Gran," repeated Jemmy, trying to look severe and roaring with laughter; "and he was to have nothing to eat but the boys' dinners, and was to drink half a cask of their beer every day. And so then the preparations were made for the two weddings, and there were hampers, and potted things, and sweet things, and nuts, and postage-stamps, and all manner of things. And so they were so jolly, that they let the Tartar out, and he was jolly too."

"I am glad they let him out," says my respected friend, "because he had only done his duty."

"Oh, but hadn't he overdone it, though!" cried Jemmy. "Well! And so then this boy mounted his horse, with his bride in his arms, and cantered away, and cantered on and on till he came to a certain place where he had a certain gran and a certain godfather, — not you two, you know."

"No, no," we both said.

"And there he was received with great rejoicings, and he filled the cupboard and the bookcase with gold, and he showered it out on his gran and his godfather because they were the kindest and dearest people that ever lived in this world. And so while they were sitting up to their knees in gold, a knocking was heard at the street door, and who should it be but Bobbo, also on horseback with his bride in his arms, and what had he come to say but that he would take (at double rent) all the lodgings forever, that were not wanted by this boy and this gran and this godfather, and that they would all live together, and all be happy! And so they were, and so it never ended!"

"And was there no quarrelling?" asked my respected friend, as Jemmy sat upon her lap and hugged her.

"No! Nobody ever quarrelled."

"And did the money never melt away?"

"No! Nobody could ever spend it all."

"And did none of them ever grow older?"

"No! Nobody ever grew older after that."

ON THE WAY TO GRETNA GREEN

THE RUNAWAY COUPLE

XX

ON THE WAY TO GRETNA GREEN

HARRY was eight and Norah was seven. They lived on Shooters Hill, six or seven miles from London. Harry's father, Mr. Walmer, had a big place called the Elms. The children read fairy-stories and delighted in princes and dragons and wicked enchanters, and kings who had fair daughters and offered them to any knights who were brave enough to come and take them. And they liked to read about lovers who ran away to Gretna Green and were married and lived happily ever after. Just where Gretna Green was they didn't know, but it must be a very romantic place to run away to. Cobbs, the gardener, heard them talking about it all as they sat under a tree. They intended to keep bees and a cow, and live on milk and honey.

Cobbs left Mr. Walmer, and went to work at the Holly Tree Inn up in Yorkshire. One day the coach drew up and two little passengers got out. Harry and Norah were on their way to Gretna Green.

"We'll stop here," said Harry to the landlord. "Chops and cherry pudding for two." Then they went to the sitting-room.

Cobbs found them there. Master Harry, on an enormous

sofa, was drying the eyes of Miss Norah with his pocket-handkerchief. Their little legs were entirely off the floor.

"I see you a-getting out, sir," said Cobbs. "I thought it was you. I thought I couldn't be mistaken in your height and figure. What's the object of your journey, sir? Matrimonial?"

"We are going to be married, Cobbs, at Gretna Green. We have run away on purpose. Norah has been in low spirits, Cobb, but she'll be happy now that we have found you to be our friend."

"Thank you, sir, and thank *you*, miss, for your good opinion. Did you bring any luggage with you?"

The lady had got a parasol, a smelling-bottle, some buttered toast, eight peppermint drops, and a small hair-brush. The gentleman had got half a dozen yards of string, a knife, three or four sheets of writing-paper, an orange, and a china mug with his name on it.

"What may be the exact natur of your plans, sir?" said Cobb.

"To go on," said the boy, "in the morning and be married to-morrow."

"Just so, sir," said Cobb. "Would it meet your views if I was to accompany you?"

When Cobbs said this, they both jumped for joy again, and cried out: "Oh, yes, Cobbs, yes!"

"Well, sir," said Cobbs, "if you will excuse my having to give an opinion, what I should recommend would be this. I'm acquainted with a pony, sir, which, put in a phaeton which I could borrow, would take you and Mrs. Harry Walmer Junior (myself driving, if you approved), to the end of your journey in a very short space of time."

They clapped their hands and jumped for joy.

"Is there anything you want, just at present, sir?"

"We should like some cakes after dinner," answered Master Harry, "and two apples and jam. With dinner we should have toast and water. But Norah has been accustomed to half a glass of currant wine for dessert, and so have I."

"It shall be ordered at the bar, sir," said Cobbs.

"Cobbs, are there any good walks in this neighborhood?"

"Begging your pardon, sir," said Cobbs, "there is Love Lane. And a pleasant walk it is, and proud shall I be to show it to yourself and Mrs. Harry Walmer Junior."

"Norah, dear," said Master Harry, "put on your bonnet, my sweetest darling, and we'll go there with Cobbs."

It was very pleasant walking down Love Lane gathering water-lilies, but as the afternoon came on they both became a little homesick. Master Harry kept up nobly, but Mrs. Harry Walmer Junior began to cry, "I want to go home." When Harry's father and Norah's mother appeared upon the scene, every one was happy. Harry and Norah had been on the way to Gretna Green, though they never got there.

OUR SCHOOL

XXI

OUR SCHOOL

THE children who live now are fortunate in having schools that are made for their happiness as well as for their mental improvement. Most of the schools Dickens describes were dreary places like that which Sissie Jupes attended. However, there were some memories that were not altogether unpleasant, and I enjoy reading the chapter which he entitles "Our School."

.   .   .   .

It seems as if our schools were doomed to be the sport of change. We have faint recollections of a Preparatory Day-School, which we have sought in vain, and which must have been pulled down to make a new street, ages ago. We have dim impressions, scarcely amounting to a belief, that it was over a dyer's shop. We know that you went up steps to it; that you frequently grazed your knees in doing so; that you generally got your leg over the scraper, in trying to scrape the mud off a very unsteady little shoe. The mistress of the Establishment holds no place in our memory; but, rampant on one eternal door-mat, in an eternal entry long and narrow, is a puffy pug-dog, with a personal animosity toward us, who triumphs over Time. The bark of that baleful Pug, a certain radiating way he had of snapping at our undefended legs, the ghastly grinning of his moist black muzzle and white teeth, and the insolence of his crisp tail curled like a pastoral crook, all live and flourish. From an otherwise unaccountable association of him with a fiddle, we conclude that he was of French extraction, and his name *Fidèle*. He belonged to some female, chiefly inhabiting a back parlor, whose life appears to us to have been consumed in sniffing, and in wearing a brown beaver bonnet. For her, he would sit up and balance cake upon his nose, and not eat it until twenty had been counted. To the best of our belief we were once called in to witness this performance; when, unable, even in his milder moments, to endure our presence, he instantly made at us, cake and all.

Why a something in mourning, called "Miss Frost," should still connect itself with our preparatory school, we are unable to say. We retain no impression of the beauty of Miss Frost — if she were beautiful; or of the mental fascinations of Miss Frost — if she were accomplished; yet her name and her black dress hold an enduring place in our remembrance. An equally impersonal boy, whose name has long since shaped itself unalterably into "Master Mawls," is not to be dislodged from our brain. Retaining no vindictive feeling toward Mawls — no feeling whatever, indeed — we infer that neither he nor we can have loved Miss Frost. . . .

But, the School that was Our School before the Railroad came and overthrew it, was quite another sort of place. We were old enough to be put into Virgil when we went there, and to get prizes for a variety of polishing on which the rust has long accumulated. It was a school of some celebrity in its neighborhood — nobody could have said why — and we had the honor to attain and hold the eminent position of first boy. The master was supposed among us to know nothing, and one of the ushers was supposed to know everything. We are still inclined to think the first-named supposition perfectly correct.

We have a general idea that its subject had been in the leather trade, and had bought us — meaning Our School — of another proprietor who was immensely learned. Whether this belief had any real foundation, we are not likely ever to know now. The only branches of education with which he showed the least acquaintance were ruling and corporally punishing. He was always ruling ciphering-books with a bloated mahogany ruler, or smiting the palms of offenders with the same diabolical instrument, or viciously drawing a pair of pantaloons tight with one of his large hands, and caning the wearer with the other. We have no doubt whatever that this occupation was the principal solace of his existence.

A profound respect for money pervaded Our School, which was, of course, derived from its Chief. We remember an idiotic goggle-eyed boy, with a big head and half-crowns without end, who suddenly appeared as a parlor-boarder, and was rumored to have come by sea from some mysterious part of the earth where his parents rolled in gold. He was usually called "Mr." by the Chief, and was said to feed in the parlor on steaks and gravy; likewise to drink currant wine. And he openly stated that if rolls and coffee were ever denied him at breakfast, he would write home to that unknown part of the globe from which he had come, and cause himself to be recalled to the regions of gold. He was put into no form or class, but learned alone, as little as he liked — and he liked very little — and there was a belief among us that this was because he was too wealthy to be "taken down." His special treatment, and our vague association of him with the sea, and with storms, and sharks, and coral reefs, occasioned the wildest legends to be circulated as his history. A tragedy in blank verse was written on the subject — if our memory does not deceive us, by the hand that now chronicles these recollections — in which his father figured as Pirate, and was shot for a voluminous catalogue of atrocities: first imparting to his wife the secret of the cave in which his wealth was stored, and from which his only son's half-crowns now issued. Dumbledon (the boy's name) was represented as "yet unborn" when his brave father met his fate; and the despair and grief of Mrs. Dumbledon at that calamity was movingly shadowed forth as having weakened the parlor-boarder's mind. This production was received with great favor, and was twice performed with closed doors in the dining-room. But it got wind, and was seized as libellous, and brought the unlucky poet into severe affliction. Some two years afterward, all of a sudden one day, Dumbledon vanished. It was whispered that the Chief himself had taken him down to the docks, and re-shipped him for the Spanish Main; but nothing certain was ever known about his disappearance. At this hour, we cannot thoroughly disconnect him from California.

OUR SCHOOL

Our School was rather famous for mysterious pupils. There was another — a heavy young man, with a large double-cased silver watch, and a fat knife the handle of which was a perfect tool-box — who unaccountably appeared one day at a special desk of his own, erected close to that of the Chief, with whom he held familiar converse. He lived in the parlor, and went out for his walks, and never took the least notice of us — even of us, the first boy — unless to give us a deprecatory kick, or grimly to take our hat off and throw it away, when he encountered us out of doors, which unpleasant ceremony he always performed as he passed — not even condescending to stop for the purpose. Some of us believed that the classical attainments of this phenomenon were terrific, but that his penmanship and arithmetic were defective, and he had come there to mend them; others, that he was going to set up a school, and had paid the Chief "twenty-five pound down," for leave to see Our School at work. The gloomier spirits even said that he was going to buy us; against which contingency, conspiracies were set on foot for a general defection and running away. However, he never did that. After staying for a quarter during which period, though closely observed, he was never seen to do anything but make pens out of quills, write small-hand in a secret portfolio, and punch the point of the sharpest blade in his knife into his desk all over it, he too disappeared, and his place knew him no more.

There was another boy, a fair, meek boy, with a delicate complexion and rich curling hair, who, we found out, or thought we found out (we have no idea now, and probably had none then, on what grounds, but it was confidentially revealed from mouth to mouth), was the son of a Viscount who had deserted his lovely mother. It was understood that if he had his rights he would be worth twenty thousand a year. And that if his mother ever met his father she would shoot him with a silver pistol, which she carried, always loaded to the muzzle, for that purpose. He was a very suggestive topic. So was a young mulatto, who was always believed (though very amiable) to have a dagger about him somewhere. But we think they were both outshone, upon the whole, by another boy who claimed to have been born on the twenty-ninth of February, and to have only one birthday in five years. We suspect this to have been a fiction — but he lived upon it all the time he was at Our School.

The principal currency of Our School was slate pencil. It had some inexplicable value, that was never ascertained, never reduced to a standard. To have a great hoard of it, was somehow to be rich. We used to bestow it in charity, and confer it as a precious boon upon our chosen friends. When the holidays were coming, contributions were solicited for certain boys whose relatives were in India, and who were appealed for under the generic name of "Holiday-stoppers," — appropriate marks of remembrance that should enliven and cheer them in their homeless state. Personally, we always contributed these tokens of sympathy in the form of slate-pencil, and always felt that it would be a comfort and a treasure to them.

OUR SCHOOL

Our School was remarkable for white mice. Red-polls, linnets, and even canaries, were kept in desks, drawers, hat-boxes, and other strange refuges for birds, but white mice were the favorite stock. The boys trained the mice, much better than the masters trained the boys. We recall one white mouse, who lived in the cover of a Latin dictionary, who ran up ladders, drew Roman chariots, shouldered muskets, turned wheels, and even made a very creditable appearance on the stage as the Dog of Montargis. He might have achieved greater things, but for having the misfortune to mistake his way in a triumphal procession to the Capitol, when he fell into a deep inkstand, and was dyed black and drowned. The mice were the occasion of some most ingenious engineering, in the construction of their houses and instruments of performance. The famous one belonged to a company of proprietors, some of whom have since made railroads, engines, and telegraphs; the chairman has erected mills and bridges in New Zealand.

The usher at Our School, who was considered to know everything as opposed to the Chief, who was considered to know nothing, was a bony, gentle-faced, clerical-looking young man in rusty black. It was whispered that he was sweet upon one of Maxby's sisters (Maxby lived closed by, and was a day pupil), and further that he "favored Maxby." As we remember, he taught Italian to Maxby's sisters on half-holidays. He once went to the play with them, and wore a white waistcoat and a rose: which was considered among us equivalent to a declaration. We were of opinion on that occasion, that to the last moment he expected Maxby's father to ask him to dinner at five o'clock, and therefore neglected his own dinner at half-past one, and finally got none. We exaggerated in our imaginations the extent to which he punished Maxby's father's cold meat at supper; and we agreed to believe that he was elevated with wine and water when he came home. But we all liked him; for he had a good knowledge of boys, and would have made it a much better school if he had had more power. He was writing master, mathematical master, English master, made out the bills, mended the pens, and did all sorts of things. He divided the little boys with the Latin master (they were smuggled through their rudimentary books, at odd times when there was nothing else to do), and he always called at parents' houses to inquire after sick boys, because he had gentlemanly manners. He was rather musical, and on some remote quarter-day had bought an old trombone; but a bit of it was lost, and it made the most extraordinary sounds when he sometimes tried to play it of an evening. His holidays never began (on account of the bills) until long after ours; but, in the summer vacations he used to take pedestrian excursions with a knapsack; and at Christmas time, he went to see his father at Chipping Norton, who we all said (on no authority) was a dairy-fed pork-butcher. Poor fellow! He was very low all day on Maxby's sister's wedding-day, and afterward was thought to favor Maxby more than ever, though he had been expected to spite him. He has been dead these twenty years. Poor fellow!

Our remembrance of Our School presents the Latin master as a colorless, doubled-up, near-sighted man with a crutch, who was always cold, and always putting onions into his ears for deafness, and always disclosing ends of flannel under all his garments, and almost always applying a ball of pocket-handkerchief to some part of his face with a screwing action round and round. He was a very good scholar, and took great pains where he saw intelligence and a desire to learn: otherwise, perhaps not. Our memory presents him (unless teased into a passion) with as little energy as color — as having been worried and tormented into monotonous feebleness — as having had the best part of his life ground out of him in a mill of boys. We remember with terror how he fell asleep one sultry afternoon with the little smuggled class before him, and awoke not when the footstep of the Chief fell heavy on the floor; how the Chief aroused him, in the midst of a dread silence, and said: "Mr. Blinkins, are you ill, sir?"; how he blushingly replied: "Sir, rather so"; how the Chief retorted with severity: "Mr. Blinkins, this is no place to be ill in" (which was very, very true), and walked back solemn as the ghost in Hamlet, until, catching a wandering eye, he caned that boy for inattention, and happily expressed his feelings toward the Latin master through the medium of a substitute.

There was a fat little dancing-master who used to come in a gig, and taught the more advanced among us hornpipes (as an accomplishment in great social demand in after life); and there was a brisk little French master who used to come in the sunniest weather, with a handleless umbrella, and to whom the Chief was always polite, because (as we believed), if the Chief offended him, he would instantly address the Chief in French, and forever confound him before the boys with his inability to understand or reply.

There was, besides, a serving man, whose name was Phil. Our retrospective glance presents Phil as a shipwrecked carpenter, cast away upon the desert island of a school, and carrying into practice an ingenious inkling of many trades. He mended whatever was broken, and made whatever was wanted. He was general glazier, among other things, and mended all the broken windows — at the prime cost (as was darkly rumored among us) of ninepence, for every square charged three-and-six to parents. We had a high opinion of his mechanical genius, and generally held that the Chief "knew something bad of him," and on pain of divulgence enforced Phil to be his bondsman. We particularly remember that Phil had a sovereign contempt for learning; which engenders in us a respect for his sagacity, as it implies his accurate observation of the relative positions of the Chief and the ushers. He was an impenetrable man, who waited at table between whiles, and throughout "the half" kept the boxes in severe custody. He was morose, even to the Chief, and never smiled, except at breaking-up, when, in acknowledgment of the toast, "Success to Phil! Hooray!" he would slowly carve a grin out of his wooden face, where it would remain until we were all gone. Nevertheless, one time when we had the scarlet fever in the school, Phil nursed all the sick boys of his own accord, and was like a mother to them.

OUR SCHOOL

There was another school not far off, and of course Our School could have nothing to say to that school. It is mostly the way with schools, whether of boys or men. Well! the railway has swallowed up ours, and the locomotives now run smoothly over its ashes.

> "So fades and languishes, grows dim and dies,
>   All that this world is proud of."

— and is not proud of, too. It had little reason to be proud of Our School, and has done much better since in that way, and will do far better yet.

ALICIA IN WONDERLAND

XXII

ALICIA IN WONDERLAND

WE all know Lewis Carroll's *Alice in Wonderland*. Dickens had an Alice too who was worth knowing. Her wonderland was a plain little house in London. Her father, Mr. Watkins, was a poorly paid government clerk who found it hard to support his large family. Her mother found life too much for her nerves. So Alice had to take the responsibility for the family happiness. While other people were worrying, she tried to make things pleasant.

But fortunately Alice had such a fortunate disposition that she could live in London and in Wonderland at the same time. In Wonderland, her father, Mr. Watkins, was king, and Mrs. Watkins was queen, and Mr. Pickles the fish-dealer was a great merchant of untold wealth. Alice had a doll who was a duchess, to whom she told her troubles, and with whom she consulted about the fashions. The duchess was a very proud and sympathetic person indeed.

So it was very natural that Alice should have a visit from her fairy godmother. The unusual thing was that she took the advice that was given her, and so got out of trouble instead of getting into it through heedlessness, as most people do in the fairy-stories. Alice was a very wise little girl; in my judgment she was almost as wise as her godmother. Indeed, it sometimes requires more wisdom to take good advice than to give it.

.   .   .   .

There was once a king, and he had a queen; and he was the manliest of his sex, and she was the loveliest of hers. The king was, in his private profession, under government. The queen's father had been a medical man out of town.

They had nineteen children, and were always having more. Seventeen of these children took care of the baby; and Alicia, the eldest, took care of them all. Their ages varied from seven years to seven months.

Let us now resume our story.

One day the king was going to the office, when he stopped at the fishmonger's to buy a pound and a half of salmon, not too near the tail, which the queen (who was a careful housekeeper) had requested him to send home. Mr. Pickles, the fishmonger, said, "Certainly, sir, is there any other article? Good morning."

The king went on toward the office in a melancholy mood; for quarter-day was such a long way off, and several of the dear children were growing out of their clothes. He had not proceeded far, when Mr. Pickles's errand-boy came running after him, and said, "Sir, you didn't notice the old lady in our shop."

"What old lady?" inquired the king. "I saw none."

Now, the king had not seen any old lady, because this old lady had been invisible to him, though visible to Mr. Pickles's boy. Probably because he messed and splashed the water about to that degree, and flapped the pairs of soles down in that violent manner, that, if she had not been visible to him, he would have spoiled her clothes.

Just then the old lady came trotting up. She was dressed in shot silk of the richest quality, smelling of dried lavender.

"King Watkins the First, I believe?" said the old lady.

"Watkins," replied the king, "is my name."

"Papa, if I am not mistaken, of the beautiful Princess Alicia?" said the old lady.

"And of eighteen other darlings," replied the king.

"Listen. You are going to the office," said the old lady.

It instantly flashed upon the king that she must be a fairy, or how could she know that?

"You are right," said the old lady, answering his thoughts. "I am the good Fairy Grandmarina. Attend! When you return home to dinner, politely invite the Princess Alicia to have some of the salmon you bought just now."

"It may disagree with her," said the king.

The old lady became so very angry at this absurd idea, that the king was quite alarmed, and humbly begged her pardon.

"We hear a great deal too much about this thing disagreeing, and that thing disagreeing," said the old lady, with the greatest contempt it was possible to express. "Don't be greedy. I think you want it all yourself."

The king hung his head under this reproof, and said he wouldn't talk about things disagreeing any more.

"Be good, then," said the Fairy Grandmarina, "and

don't! When the beautiful Princess Alicia consents to partake of the salmon — as I think she will — you will find she will leave a fish-bone on her plate. Tell her to dry it, and to rub it, and to polish it till it shines like mother-of-pearl, and to take care of it as a present from me."

"Is that all?" asked the king.

"Don't be impatient, sir," returned the Fairy Grandmarina, scolding him severely. "Don't catch people short before they have done speaking. Just the way with you grown-up persons. You are always doing it."

The king again hung his head, and said he wouldn't do so any more.

"Be good, then," said the Fairy Grandmarina, "and don't! Tell the Princess Alicia, with my love, that the fishbone is a magic present which can only be used once; but that it will bring her, that once, whatever she wishes for, PROVIDED SHE WISHES FOR IT AT THE RIGHT TIME. That is the message. Take care of it."

The king was beginning, "Might I ask the reason?" when the fairy became absolutely furious.

"*Will* you be good, sir?" she exclaimed, stamping her foot on the ground. "The reason for this, and the reason for that, indeed! You are always wanting the reason. No reason. There! Hoity toity me! I am sick of your grown-up reasons."

The king was extremely frightened by the old lady's flying into such a passion, and said he was very sorry to have offended her, and he wouldn't ask for reasons any more.

"Be good, then," said the old lady, "and don't!"

ALICIA IN WONDERLAND

With those words Grandmarina vanished, and the king went on and on and on, till he came to the office. There he wrote and wrote and wrote, till it was time to go home again. Then he politely invited the Princess Alicia, as the fairy had directed him, to partake of the salmon. And when she had enjoyed it very much, he saw the fish-bone on her plate, as the fairy had told him he would, and he delivered the fairy's message, and the Princess Alicia took care to dry the bone, and to rub it, and to polish it till it shone like mother-of-pearl.

And so, when the queen was going to get up in the morning, she said, "Oh, dear me, dear me; my head, my head!" and then she fainted away.

The Princess Alicia, who happened to be looking in at the chamber-door asking about breakfast, was very much alarmed when she saw her royal mamma in this state, and she rang the bell for Peggy, which was the name of the lord chamberlain. But remembering where the smelling-bottle was, she climbed on the chair and got it; and after that she climbed on another chair by the bedside, and held the smelling-bottle to the queen's nose; and after that she jumped down and got some water; and after that she jumped up again and wetted the queen's forehead; and in short, when the lord chamberlain came in, that dear old woman said to the little princess, "What a trot you are! I couldn't have done it better myself!"

But that was not the worst of the good queen's illness. Oh, no! She was very ill indeed for a long time. The Princess Alicia kept the seventeen young princes and princesses quiet, and dressed and undressed and danced the baby, and made the kettle boil, and heated the soup, and swept the hearth, and poured out the medicine, and nursed the queen, and did all that ever she could, and was as busy, busy, busy as busy could be; for there were not many servants at that place for three reasons: because the king was short of money, because a rise in his office never seemed to come, and because quarter-day was so far off that it looked almost as far off and as little as one of the stars.

But on the morning when the queen fainted away, where was the magic fish-bone? Why, there it was in the Princess Alicia's pocket! She had almost taken it out to bring the queen to life again, when she put it back, and looked for the smelling-bottle.

After the queen had come out of her swoon that morning and was dozing, the Princess Alicia hurried up-stairs to tell a most particular secret to a most particular confidential friend of hers, who was a duchess. People did suppose her to be a doll, but she was really a duchess, though nobody knew it except the princess.

This most particular secret was the secret about the magic fish-bone, the history of which was well known to the duchess, because the princess told her everything. The princess kneeled down by the bed on which the duchess was lying, full-dressed and wide awake, and whispered the secret to her. The duchess smiled and nodded. People might have supposed that she never smiled and nodded; but she often did, though nobody knew it except the princess.

Then the Princess Alicia hurried down-stairs again, to keep watch in the queen's room. She often kept watch by herself in the queen's room; but every evening, while the illness lasted, she sat there watching with the king. And every evening the king sat looking at her with a cross look, wondering why she never brought out the magic fish-bone. As often as she noticed this, she ran up-stairs, whispered the secret to the duchess over again, and said to the duchess, "They think we children never have a reason or a meaning!" And the duchess, though the most fashionable duchess that ever was heard of, winked her eye.

"Alicia," said the king, one evening when she wished him good night.

"Yes, papa."

"What is become of your magic fish-bone?"

"In my pocket, papa!"

"I thought you had lost it?"

"Oh no, papa."

"Or forgotten it?"

"No, indeed, papa."

And so another time the dreadful little snapping pug-dog, next door, made a rush at one of the young princes as he stood on the steps coming home from school, and terrified him out of his wits; and he put his hand through a pane of glass, and bled, bled, bled. When the seventeen other young princes and princesses saw him bleed, bleed, bleed, they were terrified out of their wits too, and screamed themselves black in their seventeen faces all at once. But the Princess Alicia put her

[231]

hands over all their seventeen mouths, one after another, and persuaded them to be quiet because of the sick queen. And then she put the wounded prince's hand in a basin of fresh cold water, while they stared with their twice seventeen are thirty-four, put down four and carry three, eyes, and then she looked in the hand for bits of glass, and there were fortunately no bits of glass there. And then she said to two chubby-legged princes, who were sturdy though small, "Bring me in the royal rag-bag: I must snip and stitch and cut and contrive." So these two young princes tugged at the royal rag-bag, and lugged it in; and the Princess Alicia sat down on the floor, with a large pair of scissors and a needle and thread, and snipped and stitched and cut and contrived, and made a bandage, and put it on, and it fitted beautifully; and so when it was all done, she saw the king her papa looking on by the door.

"Alicia."

"Yes, papa."

"What have you been doing?"

"Snipping, stitching, cutting, and contriving, papa."

"Where is the magic fish-bone?"

"In my pocket, papa."

"I thought you had lost it?"

"Oh no, papa!"

"Or forgotten it?"

"No, indeed, papa."

After that, she ran up-stairs to the duchess, and told her what had passed, and told her the secret over again: and the duchess shook her flaxen curls, and laughed with her rosy lips.

Well! and so another time the baby fell under the grate. The seventeen young princes and princesses were used to it; for they were almost always falling under the grate or down the stairs; but the baby was not used to it yet, and it gave him a swelled face and a black eye. The way the poor little darling came to tumble was, that he was out of the Princess Alicia's lap just as she was sitting, in a great coarse apron that quite smothered her, in front of the kitchen fire, beginning to peel the turnips for the broth for dinner; and the way she came to be doing that was, that the king's cook had run away that morning with her own true love, who was a very tall but very tipsy soldier. Then the seventeen young princes and princesses, who cried at every thing that happened, cried and roared. But the Princess Alicia (who couldn't help crying a little herself) quietly called to them to be still, on account of not throwing back the queen up-stairs, who was fast getting well, and said: "Hold your tongues, you wicked little monkeys, every one of you, while I examine baby!" Then she examined baby, and found that he hadn't broken anything; and she held cold iron to his poor dear eye, and smoothed his poor dear face, and he presently fell asleep in her arms. Then she said to the seventeen princes and princesses: "I am afraid to let him down yet, lest he should wake and feel pain; be good, and you shall all be cooks." They jumped for joy when they heard that, and began making themselves cooks' caps out of old newspapers.

So to one she gave the salt-box, and to one she gave the barley, and to one she gave the herbs, and to one she gave the turnips, and to one she gave the carrots, and to one she gave the onions, and to one she gave the spice-box, till they were all cooks, and all running about at work, she sitting in the middle, smothered in the great coarse apron, nursing baby. By and by the broth was done; and the baby woke up, smiling like an angel, and was trusted to the sedatest princess to hold, while the other princes and princesses were squeezed into a far-off corner to look at the Princess Alicia turning out the saucepanful of broth, for fear (as they were always getting into trouble) they should get splashed and scalded. When the broth came tumbling out, steaming beautifully, and smelling like a nosegay good to eat, they clapped their hands. That made the baby clap his hands; and that, and his looking as if he had a comic toothache, made all the princes and princesses laugh. So the Princess Alicia said: "Laugh and be good; and after dinner we will make him a nest on the floor in a corner, and he shall sit in his nest and see a dance of eighteen cooks." That delighted the young princes and princesses, and they ate up all the broth, and washed up all the plates and dishes, and cleared away, and pushed the table into a corner; and then they in their cooks' caps, and the Princess Alicia in the smothering coarse apron that belonged to the cook that had run away with her own true love that was the very tall but very tipsy soldier, danced a dance of eighteen cooks before the angelic baby, who forgot his swelled face and his black eye, and crowed with joy.

And so then, once more the Princess Alicia saw King Watkins the First, her father, standing in the doorway looking on, and he said, "What have you been doing, Alicia?"

"Cooking and contriving, papa."

"What else have you been doing, Alicia?"

"Keeping the children light-hearted, papa."

"Where is the magic fish-bone, Alicia?"

"In my pocket, papa."

"I thought you had lost it?"

"Oh no, papa."

"Or forgotten it?"

"No, indeed, papa."

The king then sighed so heavily, and seemed so low-spirited, and sat down so miserably, leaning his head upon his hand, and his elbow upon the kitchen-table pushed away in the corner, that the seventeen princes and princesses crept softly out of the kitchen, and left him alone with the Princess Alicia and the angelic baby.

"What is the matter, papa?"

"I am dreadfully poor, my child."

"Have you no money at all, papa?"

"None, my child."

"Is there no way of getting any, papa?"

"No way," said the king. "I have tried very hard, and I have tried all ways."

When she heard these last words, the Princess Alicia began to put her hand into the pocket where she kept the magic fish-bone.

"Papa," said she, "when we have tried very hard, and tried all ways, we must have done our very, very best?"

"No doubt, Alicia."

"When we have done our very, very best, papa, and that is not enough, then I think the right time must have come for asking help of others." This was the very secret connected with the magic fish-bone, which she had found out for herself from the good Fairy Grandmarina's words, and which she had so often whispered to her beautiful and fashionable friend, the duchess.

So she took out of her pocket the magic fish-bone that had been dried and rubbed and polished till it shone like mother-of-pearl; and she gave it one little kiss, and wished it was quarter-day. And immediately it *was* quarter-day; and the king's quarter's salary came rattling down the chimney, and bounced into the middle of the floor.

But this was not half of what happened — no, not a quarter; for immediately afterward the good Fairy Grandmarina came riding in, with a carriage and four (peacocks), with Mr. Pickles's boy up behind, dressed in silver and gold, with a cocked hat, powdered hair, pink silk stockings, a jewelled cane, and a nosegay. Down jumped Mr. Pickles's boy, with his cocked hat in his hand, and wonderfully polite (being entirely changed by enchantment), and handed Grandmarina out; and there she stood, in her rich shot silk smelling of dried lavender, fanning herself with a sparkling fan.

"Alicia, my dear," said this charming old fairy, "how do you do? I hope I see you pretty well? Give me a kiss."

ALICIA IN WONDERLAND

The Princess Alicia embraced her; and then Grandmarina turned to the king, and said rather sharply, "Are you
good?"

The king said he hoped so.

"I suppose you know the reason *now* why my goddaugh-
ter here," kissing the princess again, "did not apply to the
fish-bone sooner?" said the fairy.

The king made a shy bow.

"Ah! but you didn't *then?*" said the fairy.

The king made a shyer bow.

"Any more reasons to ask for?" said the fairy.

The king said, No, and he was very sorry.

"Be good, then," said the fairy, "and live happy ever
afterward."

Then Grandmarina waved her fan, and the queen came
in most splendidly dressed; and the seventeen young princes
and princesses, no longer grown out of their clothes, came
in, newly fitted out from top to toe, with tucks in everything
to admit of its being let out. After that, the fairy tapped the
Princess Alicia with her fan; and the smothering coarse apron
flew away, and she appeared exquisitely dressed, like a little
bride, with a wreath of orange flowers and a silver veil. After
that, the kitchen dresser changed of itself into a wardrobe,
made of beautiful woods and gold and looking-glass, which
was full of dresses of all sorts, all for her and all exactly fit-
ting her. After that, the angelic baby came in, running alone,
with his face and eye not a bit the worse, but much the better.
Then Grandmarina begged to be introduced to the duchess;

and, when the duchess was brought down, many compliments passed between them.

A little whispering took place between the fairy and the duchess; and then the fairy said out loud, "Yes, I thought she would have told you." Grandmarina then turned to the king and queen, and said: "We are going in search of Prince Certainpersonio. The pleasure of your company is requested at the church in half an hour precisely." So she and the Princess Alicia got into the carriage; and Mr. Pickles's boy handed in the duchess, who sat by herself on the opposite seat; and then Mr. Pickles's boy put up the steps and got up behind, and the peacocks flew away with their tails behind.

Prince Certainpersonio was sitting by himself, eating barley-sugar, and waiting to be ninety. When he saw the peacocks, followed by the carriage, coming in at the window, it immediately occurred to him that something uncommon was going to happen.

"Prince," said Grandmarina, "I bring you your bride."

The moment the fairy said those words, Prince Certainpersonio's face left off being sticky, and his jacket and corduroys changed to peach-bloom velvet, and his hair curled, and a cap and feather flew in like a bird and settled on his head. He got into the carriage by the fairy's invitation; and there he renewed his acquaintance with the duchess, whom he had seen before.

In the church were the prince's relations and friends, and the Princess Alicia's relations and friends, and the seventeen princes and princesses, and the baby, and a crowd of the neighbors. The marriage was beautiful beyond expression. The duchess was bridesmaid, and beheld the ceremony from the pulpit, where she was supported by the cushion of the desk.

Grandmarina gave a magnificent wedding-feast afterward, in which there was everything and more to eat, and everything and more to drink. The wedding-cake was delicately ornamented with white satin ribbons, frosted silver, and white lilies, and was forty-two yards round.

When Grandmarina had drunk her love to the young couple, and Prince Certainpersonio had made a speech, and everybody had cried, hip, hip, hip, hurrah! Grandmarina announced to the king and queen that in future there would be eight quarter-days in every year, except leap-year, when there would be ten. She then turned to Certainpersonio and Alicia, and said, "My dears, you will have thirty-five children, and they will be good and beautiful. Seventeen of your children will be boys, and eighteen girls. The hair of the whole of your children will curl naturally. They will never have the measles, and will have recovered from the whooping-cough before being born."

On hearing such good news everybody cried out, "Hip, hip, hip, hurrah!" again.

"It only remains, said Grandmarina in conclusion, "to make an end of the fish-bone."

THE INFANT PHENOMENON

XXIII

THE INFANT PHENOMENON

IN our day the moving picture and the radio have made it possible for the people who live in the city and the people who live in the country to see and hear the same things. Our amusements are very much alike. But it was not so in Dickens's day. The great actors were in the theatres of the large cities; but companies of strolling players were on the roads. They carried their stage scenery with them and did their own advertising. They did not have to compete with those who could act better.

Dickens enjoyed these cheerful wanderers who went about giving entertainments to people who were easily pleased. When Nicholas Nickleby and his friend Smike were trudging along on the road from London to Portsmouth they fell in with Mr. Vincent Crummles and his dramatic company. Nicholas had almost come to the end of the little money with which he started, and he was very glad when Mr. Crummles invited him to share his supper at the inn. When Nicholas had told Mr. Crummles his story he was invited to join the company, at a salary which while not large was sufficient to keep him from starving. In this way he became acquainted with the Infant Phenomenon. She was the daughter of Mr. and Mrs. Crummles and was the pride of the family. Nicholas was introduced to her when they came to the theatre in the next town. It was a very dingy little theatre on a back street. Mrs. Crummles led the way to the stage.

There bounded on to the stage from some mysterious inlet, a little girl in a dirty white frock with tucks up to the knees, short trousers, sandled shoes, white spencer, pink gauze bonnet, green veil, and curl-papers; who turned a pirouette, cut twice in the air, turned another pirouette, then, looking off at the opposite wing, shrieked, bounded forward to within six inches of the footlights, and fell into a beautiful attitude of terror, as a shabby gentleman in an old pair of buff slippers came in at one powerful slide, and chattering his teeth, fiercely brandished a walking-stick.

"They are going through the Indian Savage and the Maiden," said Mrs. Crummles.

"Oh!" said the manager, "the little ballet interlude. Very good, go on. A little this way, if you please, Mr. Johnson. That'll do. Now!"

The manager clapped his hands as a signal to proceed, and the savage, becoming ferocious, made a slide toward the maiden; but the maiden avoided him in six twirls, and came down at the end of the last one upon the very points of her toes. This seemed to make some impression upon the savage; for, after a little more ferocity and chasing of the maiden into corners, he began to relent, and stroked his face several times with his right thumb and forefinger, thereby intimating that he was struck with admiration of the maiden's beauty. Acting upon the impulse of this passion, he (the savage) began to hit himself severe thumps in the chest, and to exhibit other indications of being desperately in love, which being rather a prosy proceeding, was very likely the cause of the maiden's falling asleep; whether it was or no, asleep she did fall, sound as a church, on a sloping bank, and the savage perceiving it, leaned his left ear on his left hand, and nodded sideways, to intimate to all whom it might concern that she *was* asleep, and no shamming. Being left to himself, the savage had a dance, all alone. Just as he left off, the maiden woke up, rubbed her eyes, got off the bank, and had a dance all alone too — such a dance that the savage looked on in ecstasy all the while, and when it was done, plucked from a neighboring tree some botanical curiosity, resembling a small pickled cabbage, and offered it to the maiden, who at first wouldn't have it, but on the savage shedding tears relented. Then the savage jumped for joy; then the maiden jumped for rapture at the sweet smell of the pickled cabbage. Then the savage and the maiden danced violently together, and, finally, the savage dropped down on one knee, and the maiden stood on one leg upon his other knee; thus concluding the ballet, and leaving the spectators in a state of pleasing uncertainty, whether she would ultimately marry the savage, or return to her friends.

"Very well indeed," said Mr. Crummles; "bravo!"

"Bravo!" cried Nicholas, resolved to make the best of everything. "Beautiful!"

"This, sir," said Mr. Vincent Crummles, bringing the

maiden forward, "this is the Infant Phenomenon — Miss Ninetta Crummles."

"Your daughter?" inquired Nicholas.

"My daughter — my daughter," replied Mr. Vincent Crummles; "the idol of every place we go into, sir. We have complimentary letters about this girl, sir, from the nobility and gentry of almost every town in England."

"I am not surprised at that," said Nicholas; "she must be quite a natural genius."

"Quite a — !" Mr. Crummles stopped; language was not powerful enough to describe the Infant Phenomenon. "I'll tell you what, sir," he said; "the talent of this child is not to be imagined. She must be seen, sir — seen — to be ever so faintly appreciated. There; go to your mother, my dear."

"May I ask how old she is?" inquired Nicholas.

"You may, sir," replied Mr. Crummles, looking steadily in his questioner's face, as some men do when they have doubts about being implicitly believed in what they are going to say. "She is ten years of age, sir."

"Not more?"

"Not a day."

"Dear me!" said Nicholas, "it's extraordinary."

It was; for the Infant Phenomenon, though of short stature, had a comparatively aged countenance, and had moreover been precisely the same age — not perhaps to the full extent of the memory of the oldest inhabitant, but certainly for five good years. But she had been kept up late every night, and put upon an unlimited allowance of gin and water from infancy, to prevent her growing tall, and perhaps this system of training had produced in the Infant Phenomenon these additional phenomena.

Nicholas was invited to dinner with the Crummles family at their lodgings. Mrs. Crummles, who always talked as if she were on the stage, received him in a most dignified way.

"You are welcome," said Mrs. Crummles, turning round to Nicholas when they reached the bow-windowed front room on the first floor.

Nicholas bowed his acknowledgments, and was unfeignedly glad to see the cloth laid.

"We have but a shoulder of mutton with onion sauce," said Mrs. Crummles, in the same charnel-house voice; "but such as our dinner is, we beg you to partake of it."

"You are very good," replied Nicholas, "I shall do it ample justice."

"Vincent," said Mrs. Crummles, "what is the hour?"

"Five minutes past dinner-time," said Mr. Crummles.

Mrs. Crummles rang the bell. "Let the mutton and onion sauce appear."

The slave who attended upon Mr. Bulph's lodgers disappeared, and after a short interval reappeared with the festive banquet. Nicholas and the Infant Phenomenon opposed each other at the pembroke-table, and Smike and the Master Crummleses dined on the sofa-bedstead.

"Are they very theatrical people here?" asked Nicholas.

"No," replied Mr. Crummles, shaking his head, "far from it — far from it."

"I pity them," observed Mrs. Crummles.

"So do I," said Nicholas; "if they have no relish for the atrical entertainments, properly conducted."

"Then they have none, sir," rejoined Mr. Crummles. "To the Infant's benefit, last year, on which occasion she repeated three of her most popular characters, and also appeared in the Fairy Porcupine, as originally performed by her, there was a house of no more than four-pound-twelve."

" Is it possible?" cried Nicholas.

"And two pound of that was trust, pa," said the Phenomenon.

"And two pound of that was trust," repeated Mr. Crummles.

The public did not always appreciate the genius of the Infant Phenomenon, but that made no difference to the admiring father. When Nicholas suggested that perhaps a boy phenomenon might be added to the company, Mr. Crummles answered solemnly: "There is only one Phenomenon, sir, and that is a girl."

A CHRISTMAS TREE

XXIV

A CHRISTMAS TREE

MOST people love Christmas trees, but the first Christmas trees one sees are the most wonderful of all. Dickens tells about the tree he saw when he was just the right age to appreciate its wonderfulness. He never afterward saw anything that was equal to it in magnificence. All sorts of objects clustered on the branches like magic fruit. And the best thing about it all was that many of these things were for him.

    .   .   .   .

All toys at first, I find. Up yonder, among the green holly and red berries, is the Tumbler with his hands in his pockets, who wouldn't lie down, but whenever he was put upon the floor, persisted in rolling his fat body about, until he rolled himself still, and brought those lobster eyes of his to bear upon me — when I affected to laugh very much, but in my heart of hearts was extremely doubtful of him. Close beside him is that infernal snuff-box, out of which there sprang a demoniacal Counsellor in a black gown, with an obnoxious head of hair, and a red cloth mouth, wide open, who was not to be endured on any terms, but could not be put away either; for he used suddenly, in a highly magnified state, to fly out of mammoth snuff-boxes in dreams, when least expected. Nor is the frog with cobbler's wax on his tail, far

off; for there was no knowing where he wouldn't jump; and
when he flew over the candle, and came upon one's hand
with that spotted back — red on a green ground — he was
horrible. The cardboard lady in a blue-silk skirt, who was
stood up against the candlestick to dance, and whom I see
on the same branch, was milder, and was beautiful; but I
can't say as much for the larger cardboard man, who used
to be hung against the wall and pulled by a string; there was
a sinister expression in that nose of his; and when he got his
legs round his neck (which he very often did), he was ghastly,
and not a creature to be alone with.

When did that dreadful Mask first look at me? Who put
it on, and why was I so frightened that the sight of it is an
era in my life? It is not a hideous visage in itself; it is even
meant to be droll; why then were its stolid features so intol-
erable? Surely not because it hid the wearer's face. An apron
would have done as much; and though I should have preferred even the apron away, it would not have been absolutely insupportable, like the mask. Was it the immovability
of the mask? The doll's face was immovable, but I was not
afraid of *her*. Perhaps that fixed and set change coming over
a real face infused into my quickened heart some remote
suggestion and dread of the universal change that is to come
on every face and make it still? Nothing reconciled me to
it. No drummers, from whom proceeded a melancholy chirp-
ing on the turning of a handle; no regiment of soldiers, with
a mute band, taken out of a box, and fitted, one by one,
upon a stiff and lazy little set of lazy-tongs; no old woman,

made of wires and a brown-paper composition, cutting up a pie for two small children, could give me a permanent comfort, for a long time. Nor was it any satisfaction to be shown the Mask, and see that it was made of paper, or to have it locked up and be assured that no one wore it. The mere recollection of that fixed face, the mere knowledge of its existence anywhere, was sufficient to awake me in the night all perspiration and horror, with, "Oh, I know its coming! Oh, the mask!"

I never wondered what the dear old donkey with the panniers — there he is! was made of, then! His hide was real to the touch, I recollect. And the great black horse with the round red spots all over him — the horse that I could even get upon — I never wondered what had brought him to that strange condition, or thought that such a horse was not commonly seen at Newmarket. The four horses of no color, next to him, that went into the wagon of cheeses, and could be taken out and stabled under the piano, appear to have bits of fur-tippet for their tails, and other bits for their manes, and to stand on pegs instead of legs; but it was not so when they were brought home for a Christmas present. They were all right, then; neither was their harness unceremoniously nailed into their chests, as appears to be the case now. The tinkling works of the music-cart, I *did* find out, to be made of quill toothpicks and wire; and I always thought that little tumbler in his shirt-sleeves, perpetually swarming up one side of a wooden frame, and coming down, head foremost, on the other, rather a weak-minded person — though good-natured; but the Jacob's Ladder, next him, made of little squares of red wood, that went flapping and clattering over one another, each developing a different picture, and the whole enlivened by small bells, was a mighty marvel and a great delight.

Ah! The Doll's house! — of which I was not proprietor, but where I visited. I don't admire the Houses of Parliament half so much as that stone-fronted mansion with real glass windows and doorsteps, and a real balcony — greener than I ever see now, except at watering-places; and even they afford but a poor imitation. And though it *did* open all at once, the entire house-front (which was a blow, I admit, as cancelling the fiction of a staircase), it was but to shut it up again, and I could believe. Even open, there were three distinct rooms in it: a sitting-room and bedroom, elegantly furnished, and best of all, a kitchen, with uncommonly soft fire-irons, a plentiful assortment of diminutive utensils — oh, the warming-pan! — and a tin man-cook in profile, who was always going to fry two fish! What Barmecide justice have I done to the noble feasts wherein the set of wooden platters figured, each with its own peculiar delicacy, as a ham or turkey, glued tight on to it, and garnished with something green, which I recollect as moss! Could all the Temperance societies of these later days, united, give me such a tea-drinking as I have had through the means of yonder little set of blue crockery, which really would hold liquid (it ran out of the small wooden cask, I recollect, and tasted of matches), and which made tea, nectar. And if the two legs

of the ineffectual little sugar-tongs did tumble over one another, and want purpose, like Punch's hands, what does it
matter? And if I did once shriek out, as a poisoned child,
and strike the fashionable company with consternation, by
reason of having drunk a little teaspoon, inadvertently dis-
solved in too hot tea, I was never the worse for it, except by
a powder!

Upon the next branches of the tree, lower down, hard by
the green roller and miniature gardening-tools, how thick
the books begin to hang. Thin books, in themselves, at first,
but many of them, and with deliciously smooth covers of
bright red or green. What fat black letters to begin with!
"A was an Archer, and shot at a frog." Of course he was.
He was an Apple-pie also, and there he is! He was a good
many things in his time, was A, and so were most of his
friends, except X, who had so little versatility that I never
knew him to get beyond Xerxes or Xantippe — like Y, who
was always confined to a Yacht or a Yew Tree; and Z con-
demned forever to be a Zebra or a Zany. But, now, the very
tree itself changes, and becomes a bean-stalk — the mar-
vellous bean-stalk up which Jack climbed to the Giant's
house! And now, those dreadfully interesting, double-headed
giants, with their clubs over their shoulders, begin to stride
along the boughs in a perfect throng, dragging knights and
ladies home for dinner by the hair of their heads. And Jack
— how noble, with his sword of sharpness, and his shoes of
swiftness! Again those old meditations come upon me as I
gaze up at him; and I debate within myself whether there

was more than one Jack (which I am loath to believe possible), or only one genuine original admirable Jack, who achieved all the recorded exploits.

Good for Christmas time is the ruddy color of the cloak, in which — the tree making a forest of itself for her to trip through, with her basket — Little Red Riding-Hood comes to me one Christmas Eve to give me information of the cruelty and treachery of that dissembling Wolf who ate her grandmother, without making any impression on his appetite, and then ate her, after making that ferocious joke about his teeth. She was my first love. I felt that if I could have married Little Red Riding-Hood, I should have known perfect bliss. But it was not to be; and there was nothing for it but to look out the Wolf in the Noah's Ark there, and put him late in the procession on the table, as a monster who was to be degraded. Oh, the wonderful Noah's Ark! It was not found seaworthy when put in a washing-tub, and the animals were crammed in at the roof, and needed to have their legs well shaken down before they could be got in, even there — and then, ten to one but they began to tumble out at the door, which was but imperfectly fastened with a wire latch — but what was *that* against it! Consider the noble fly, a size or two smaller than the elephant: the lady-bird, the butterfly — all triumphs of art! Consider the goose, whose feet were so small, and whose balance was so indifferent, that he usually tumbled forward, and knocked down all the animal creation. Consider Noah and his family, like idiotic tobacco-stoppers; and how the leopard stuck to warm little fingers;

and how the tails of the larger animals used gradually to resolve themselves into frayed bits of string!

Hush! Again a forest, and somebody up in a tree — not Robin Hood, not Valentine, not the Yellow Dwarf (I have passed him and all Mother Bunch's wonders, without mention), but an Eastern King with a glittering scimitar and turban. By Allah! two Eastern Kings, for I see another, looking over his shoulder! Down upon the grass, at the tree's foot, lies the full length of a coal-black Giant, stretched asleep, with his head in a lady's lap; and near them is a glass box, fastened with four locks of shining steel, in which he keeps the lady prisoner when he is awake. I see the four keys at his girdle now. The lady makes signs to the two kings in the tree, who softly descend. It is the setting-in of the bright Arabian Nights.

Oh, now all common things become uncommon and enchanted to me. All lamps are wonderful; all rings are talismans. Common flower-pots are full of treasure, with a little earth scattered on the top; trees are for Ali Baba to hide in; beefsteaks are to throw down into the Valley of Diamonds, that the precious stones may stick to them, and be carried by the eagles to their nests, whence the traders, with loud cries, will scare them. Tarts are made, according to the recipe of the Vizier's son of Bussorah, who turned pastry-cook after he was set down in his drawers at the gate of Damascus; cobblers are all Mustaphas, and in the habit of sewing up people cut into four pieces, to whom they are taken blindfold.

Any iron ring let into stone is the entrance to a cave which only waits for the magician, and the little fire, and the necromancy, that will make the earth shake. All the dates imported come from the same tree as that unlucky date with whose shell the merchant knocked out the eye of the genie's invisible son. All olives are of the stock of that fresh fruit concerning which the Commander of the Faithful overheard the boy conduct the fictitious trial of the fraudulent olive merchant; all apples are akin to the apple purchased (with two others) from the Sultan's gardener for three sequins, and which the tall black slave stole from the child. All dogs are associated with the dog, really a transformed man, who jumped upon the baker's counter, and put his paw on the piece of bad money. All rice recalls the rice which the awful lady, who was a ghoul, would only peck by grains, because of her nightly feasts in the burial-place. My very rocking-horse — there he is, with his nostrils turned completely inside-out, indicative of Blood! — should have a peg in his neck, by virtue thereof to fly away with me, as the wooden horse did with the Prince of Persia, in the sight of all his father's court.

Yes, on every object that I recognize among those upper branches of my Christmas tree, I see this fairy light! When I wake in bed, at daybreak, on the cold, dark, winter mornings, the white snow dimly beheld, outside, through the frost on the window-pane, I hear Dinarzade: "Sister, sister, if you are yet awake, I pray you finish the history of the Young King of the Black Islands." Scheherazade replies:

[258]

A CHRISTMAS TREE

"If my lord the Sultan will suffer me to live another day, sister, I will not only finish that, but tell you a more wonderful story yet." Then, the gracious sultan goes out, giving no orders for the execution, and we all three breathe again.

THE SCRIBNER ILLUSTRATED CLASSICS

THE ARABIAN NIGHTS
Edited by KATE DOUGLAS WIGGIN
Illustrated by Maxfield Parrish

THE STORY OF ROLAND
by JAMES BALDWIN
Illustrated by Peter Hurd

THE STORY OF SIEGFRIED
by JAMES BALDWIN
Illustrated by Peter Hurd

DRUMS
by JAMES BOYD
Illustrated by N. C. Wyeth

A LITTLE PRINCESS
by FRANCES HODGSON BURNETT
Illustrated by Ethel Franklin Betts

THE DEERSLAYER
by JAMES FENIMORE COOPER
Illustrated by N. C. Wyeth

THE LAST OF THE MOHICANS
by JAMES FENIMORE COOPER
Illustrated by N. C. Wyeth

ROBIN HOOD
by PAUL CRESWICK
Illustrated by N. C. Wyeth

THE ENCHANTED BOOK
Edited by ALICE DALGLIESH
Illustrated by Concetta Cacciola

ROBINSON CRUSOE
by DANIEL DEFOE
Illustrated by N. C. Wyeth

THE CHILDREN OF DICKENS
by CHARLES DICKENS
Edited by Samuel McChord Crothers
Ilustrated by Jessie Willcox Smith

HANS BRINKER
by MARY MAPES DODGE
Illustrated by George W. Edwards

POEMS OF CHILDHOOD
by EUGENE FIELD
Illustrated by Maxfield Parrish

THE LITTLE SHEPHERD OF
KINGDOM COME
by JOHN FOX, JR.
Illustrated by N. C. Wyeth

GRIMM'S FAIRY TALES
Illustrated by Elenore Abbott

LONE COWBOY
by WILL JAMES
Illustrated by the author

SMOKY
by WILL JAMES
Illustrated by the author

WESTWARD HO!
by CHARLES KINGSLEY
Illustrated by N. C. Wyeth

THE BOY'S KING ARTHUR
by SIDNEY LANIER
Illustrated by N. C. Wyeth

THE SCOTTISH CHIEFS
by JANE PORTER
Illustrated by N. C. Wyeth

THE YEARLING
by MARJORIE KINNAN RAWLINGS
Illustrated by N. C. Wyeth

QUENTIN DURWARD
by SIR WALTER SCOTT
Illustrated by C. B. Chambers

THE CHILDREN'S BIBLE
by HENRY SHERMAN and CHARLES KENT
Illustrated by various artists

HEIDI
by JOHANNA SPYRI
Illustrated by Jessie Willcox Smith

A CHILD'S GARDEN OF VERSES
by ROBERT LOUIS STEVENSON
Illustrated by Jessie Willcox Smith

THE BLACK ARROW
by ROBERT LOUIS STEVENSON
Illustrated by N. C. Wyeth

DAVID BALFOUR
by ROBERT LOUIS STEVENSON
Illustrated by N. C. Wyeth

KIDNAPPED
by ROBERT LOUIS STEVENSON
Illustrated by N. C. Wyeth

TREASURE ISLAND
by ROBERT LOUIS STEVENSON
Illustrated by N. C. Wyeth

THE MYSTERIOUS ISLAND
by JULES VERNE
Illustrated by N. C. Wyeth

TWENTY THOUSAND LEAGUES UNDER THE SEA
by JULES VERNE
Illustrated by W. J. Aylward